Gold Stars®

My BIG Book of MATHS and ENGLISH

Ages 3–5

Written by
David and Penny Glover
and Betty Root

p

Helping your child

⭐ Do talk about what's on the page. Let your child know that you are sharing the activities.

⭐ Explain what has to be done on each page, and help with any recording such as colouring and joining up.

⭐ Do not become anxious if your child finds any of the activities too difficult. Young children develop and learn at different rates.

⭐ Let your child do as much or as little as he or she wishes. Do leave a page that seems to be difficult and return to it later.

⭐ It does not matter if your child does some of the pages out of turn.

⭐ The answers to the activities start on page 232.

⭐ Always be encouraging, and give plenty of praise.

⭐ Remember that the gold stars are a reward for effort as well as achievement.

Illustrated by Simon Abbott

This is a Parragon book
This edition published in 2006

Parragon
Queen Street House
4 Queen Street
BATH, BA1 1HE, UK

ISBN 1-40547-615-X
Printed in Malaysia

Contents

Contents

Contents

Contents

Contents

Count one

Point to the number.
Trace it with your finger.

Point to each picture. Count how many and write the answer in each box.

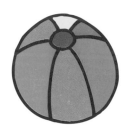

1

1

Note for parent: Introduce counting with everyday objects such as balls, shoes and animals.

Count two

Point to the number.
Trace it with your finger.

Point to each picture.
Count how many and write the answer in each box.

Note for parent: Numbers are used as labels, to number houses
for example, as well as to count 'how many'.

Draw a ring around the ladybird with two spots.

Who lives at number 2?
Write the answer on the dotted line.

John   Emma   James   Emma..................

Draw two candles on the cake.

Count three

Point to the number.
Trace it with your finger.

Point to each picture. Count how many
and write the answer in each box.

Note for parent: Before writing a number, your child should
trace over the shape several times with their finger.

Draw a ring around the ball with three spots.

Draw a ring around bus number 3.

Draw three spots on the ladybird and colour it.

One, two, three!

Point to each picture. Count each set and draw lines to match each set to a number.

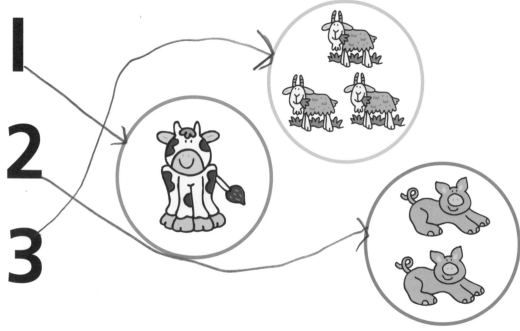

Point to each picture. Count the bricks.
Draw lines to join them to the correct number.

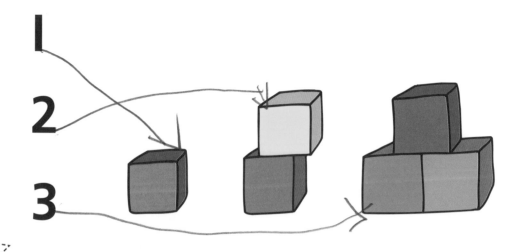

Note for parent: These pages give further practice with the numbers 1, 2 and 3.

Count the objects in each box. Write the answer in the small square. Draw lines to join the boxes with the same number.

3

2

2

1

1

3

Count four

Point to the number.
Trace it with your finger.

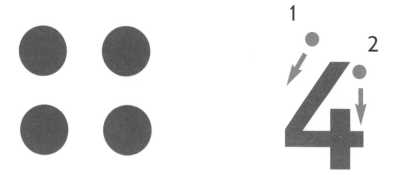

Look at each picture. Count how many candles.
Draw a ring around the correct number.
Now draw a ring around the correct number of
horse's hooves.

1   2   3   ④

1   2   3   ④

Note for parent: Always try to count real objects, pointing
as you do so. Don't just recite the number words.

Count the balloons. Draw a ring around the teddy with four balloons.

Look at the picture. Tick car number **4**.

Count five

Point to the number.
Trace it with your finger.

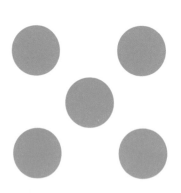

Look at the foot. Count how many toes and draw a ring around the correct number.

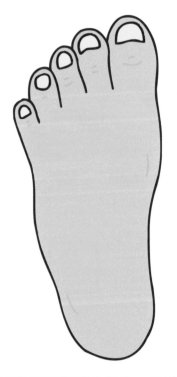

1

2

3

4

5

Note for parent: Encourage your child to use their fingers as they count.

Draw a ring around the clown with five balls.

Colour the dogs with five spots.

Draw five sausages in the pan.

Practise counting to 5

Draw lines to join the sets that have the same number in them.

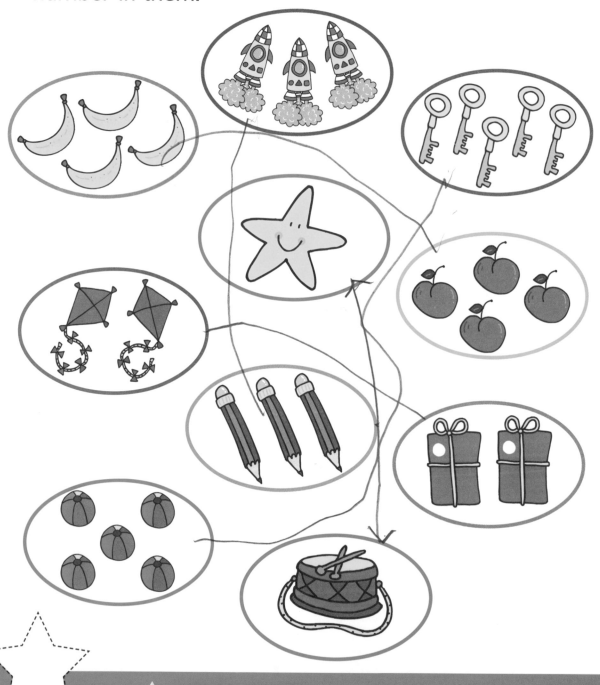

Note for parent: This activity gives further practice counting up to 5.

Look at each pair of pictures. Count the things in each box. Tick the box which has more in it. The first one has been done for you.

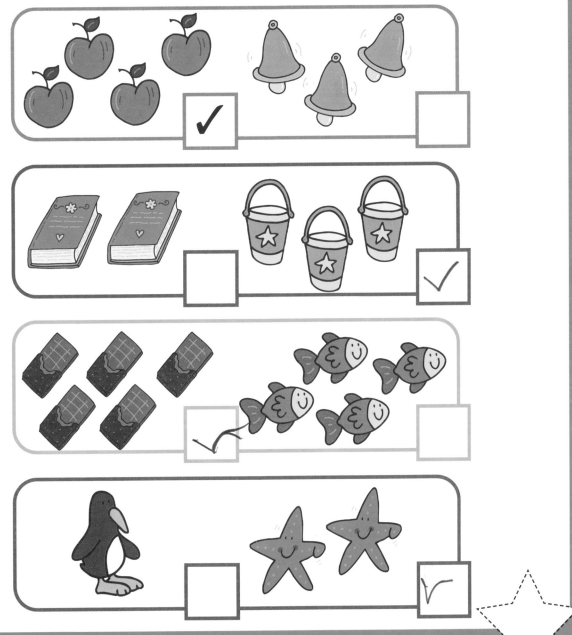

Count six

Point to the number.
Trace it with your finger.

Count the bee's legs.
Draw a ring around the
correct number.

Count the hen's eggs. Write the number in the box.

Note for parent: Practise counting with real objects; move
them around and ask if there are still the same number.

Look at the flowers. Colour the flower with six petals.

Colour six apples in the tree.

Colour the bowl with six fish.

Count seven

Point to the number.
Trace it with your finger.

Point to each present. Count how many
and write the answer in the box.

Note for parent: Think of a number between one and ten. Ask
your child to guess what it is saying the words higher and lower.

Count Snow White's dwarfs.
Count their beds. Write the
correct numbers in the boxes.

dwarfs 7   beds 7

27

Count eight

Point to the number.
Trace it with your finger.

Point to each sock. Count how many and
write the answer in the box.

Count how many spider's legs and write
the answer in the box.

Note for parent: When children count they need to
co-ordinate saying the number whilst pointing to each object.

Colour eight butterflies.

Draw a line to join the rod to duck
number 8.

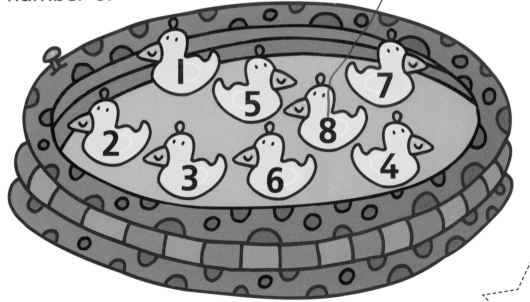

Count nine

Point to the number. Trace it with your finger.

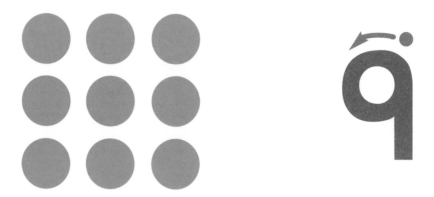

Count the marbles in the bag. Write the answer in the box.

Note for parent: This activity gives your child practice in counting up to 9.

Colour nine fish in the pond.

Count the things in each set and write the answer in the box.

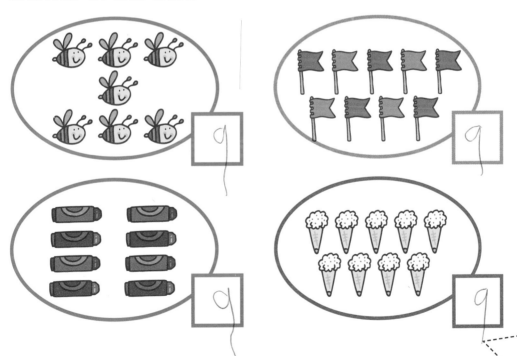

9

9

9

9

Count ten

Point to the number.
Trace it with your finger.

Look at the feet. Count how many toes and
draw a ring around the correct number.

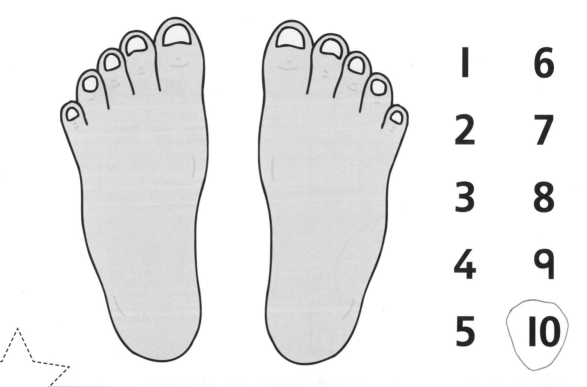

1	6
2	7
3	8
4	9
5	(10)

Note for parent: Also show your child how to count to 10 by
using all the fingers on both hands.

Colour the snake with ten spots.

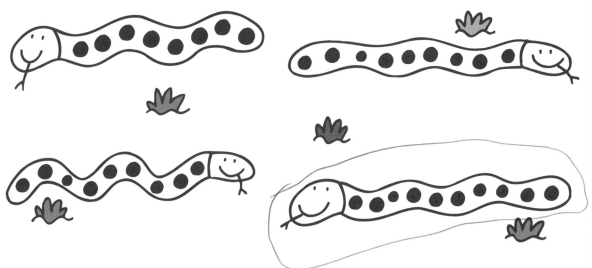

Colour the bottles on the wall. Count how many
and draw a ring around the right number.

1 2 3 4 5 6 7 8 9 10

33

How many?

Count each set and write the correct
number in each box.

Note for parent: This activity gives further practice counting up to 10.

Ten fat sausages

Count the number of sausages in each pan and write the correct number in each box.

10

Ten fat sausages sizzling in the pan,
One went pop, one went BANG!

8

Eight fat sausages sizzling in the pan,
One went pop, one went BANG!

6

Six fat sausages sizzling in the pan,
One went pop, one went BANG!

Note for parent: When your child is counting confidently to 10 in ones, introduce counting forwards and backwards in twos.

Four fat sausages sizzling in the pan,
One went pop, one went BANG!

Two fat sausages sizzling in the pan,
One went pop, one went BANG!

No fat sausages sizzling in the pan!

Making patterns

Trace over the dotted lines. Make a row underneath.

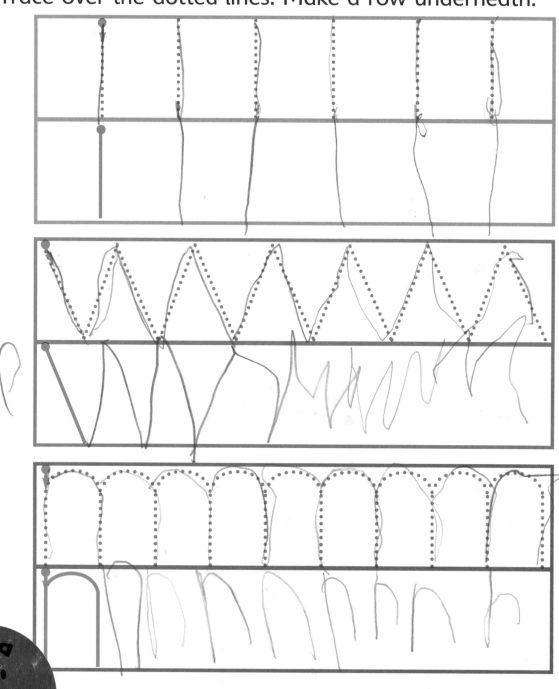

Note for parent: This activity gives practice in pencil control in preparation for letter shapes.

Go together

Start at the red dot. Draw along each path.
Try not to touch the lines.

Note for parent: Keeping between the lines helps pencil control.

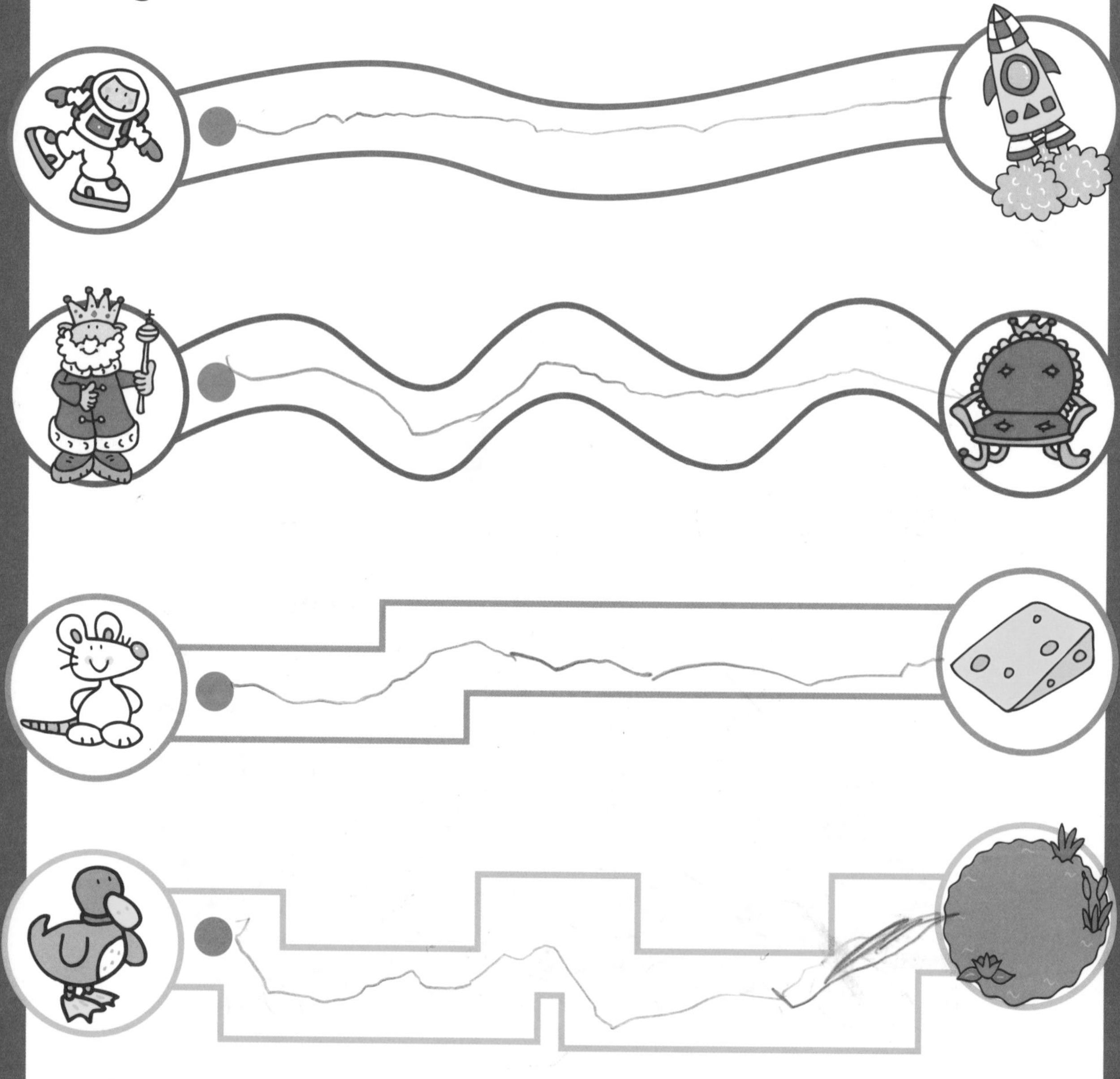

Find the balls

Find 5 balls in the picture.
Draw a circle around each one.
Finish the pattern of circles around the picture.
Colour the picture.

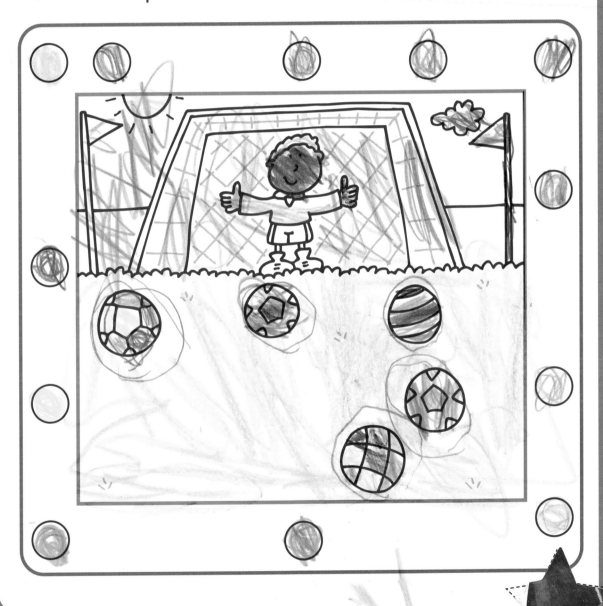

Note for parent: This activity helps children
to draw circles.

Shadows

Draw lines to join each picture to its shadow.
Try to make straight lines.
The first one has been done for you.

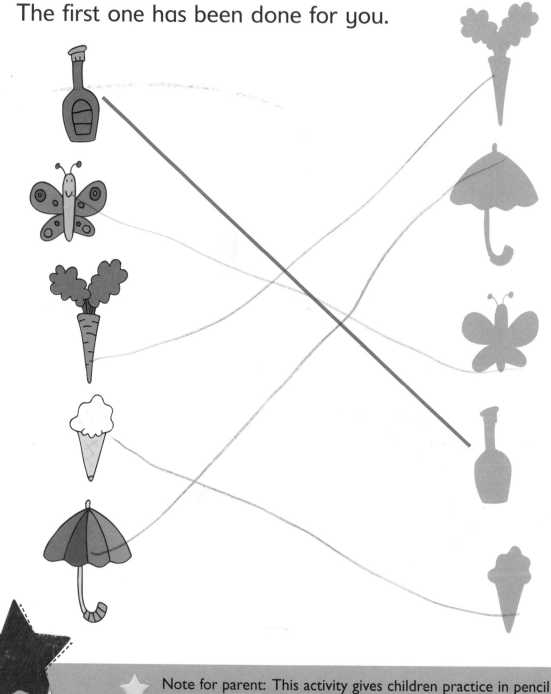

Note for parent: This activity gives children practice in pencil
control for straight and wiggly lines.

Draw lines to join each picture to its shadow.
Try to make wiggly lines.
The first one has been done for you.

A wet day

Draw over the dotted lines to finish the picture.
Colour the picture.

Note for parent: This activity helps children to use a pencil
carefully to complete pictures.

What shall I eat?

Start at the red dot. Draw along each path to find out what everyone eats.

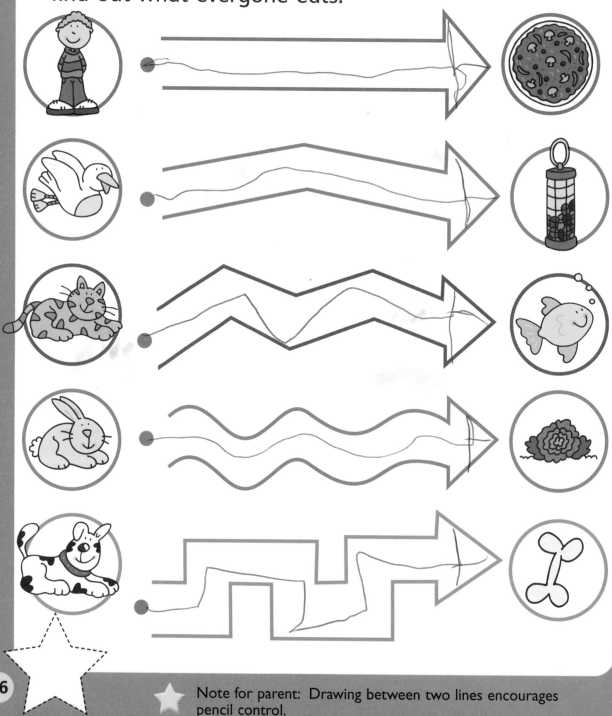

Note for parent: Drawing between two lines encourages pencil control.

Tails

Draw over the dotted lines.
Colour the animals.

Note for parent: Children need to develop a steady
hand for good writing.

Safari park

Draw over the dotted lines.
Colour the picture.

Note for parent: This activity helps children to use a pencil carefully to complete pictures.

Flying kites

Draw over the dotted lines.
Colour the kites to match the T-shirts.

Note for parent: This gives children practice in
controlling the direction of their pencil.

Trace the pattern

Trace over the dotted lines on each ball.

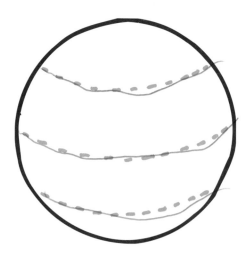

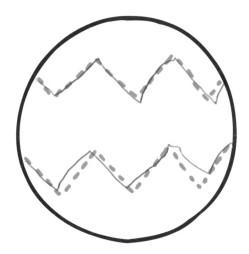

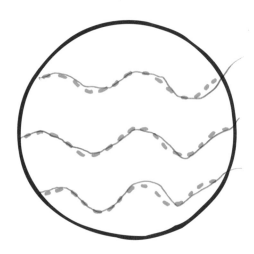

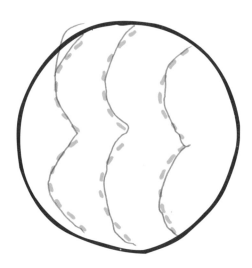

 Note for parent: This activity gives children further practice in pencil control.

Motor mazes

Trace over the dotted lines to find out which car will get to the flag first.

Note for parent: This gives children practice in controlling the direction of their pencil.

More patterns

Trace over the lines to finish the pictures.

Note for parent: This activity helps children to follow dotted lines to make a pattern.

Making letters 1

Trace over each dotted letter.

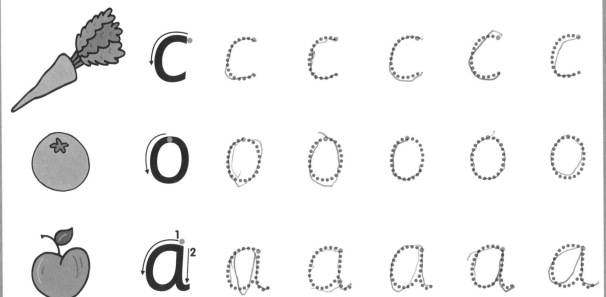

c c c c c c

o o o o o o

a a a a a a

Trace the letters to complete the words.

orange

apple

carrot

 Note for parent: This activity helps children to write the letters c, o and a.

Making letters 2

Trace over each dotted letter.

d d d d d d d

g g g g g g g

q q q q q q q

Circle the picture which begins with the letter d.

Note for parent: This activity helps children to write the letters d, g, q, b, h and p.

Trace over each dotted letter.

Say the name of each picture and write its beginning letter.

Making letters 3

Trace over each dotted letter.

  r r r r r r r

 n n n n n n n

 m m m m m m m m

Put a tick or a cross in each box. Yes ✓ No ✗

 begins with r

 begins with m

 begins with n

Note for parent: This activity helps children to write the letters r, n, m, u and y.

Trace over each dotted letter.

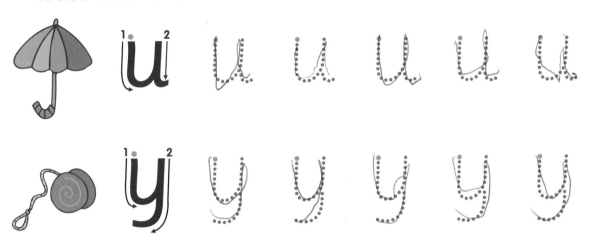

Trace the letters to complete the words.

s un

umbrella

yellow

yo-yo

Making letters 4

Trace over the dotted letters.

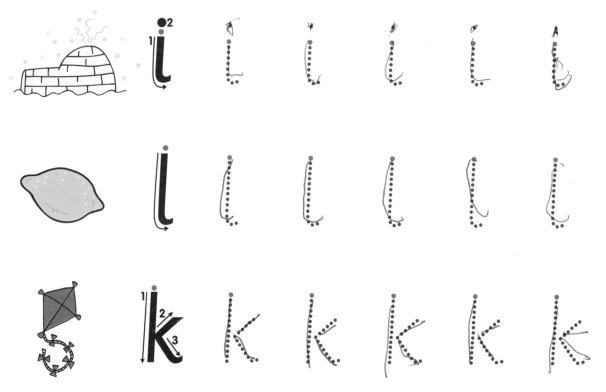

Circle the picture which begins with the letter k.

Note for parent: This activity helps children write the letters i, l, k, f, j and t.

Trace over the dotted letters.

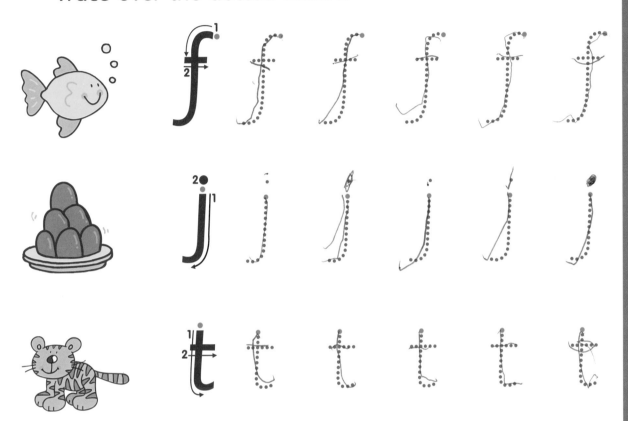

Say the name of each picture.
Cross out the letter which is wrong.

59

Making letters 5

Trace over the dotted letters.

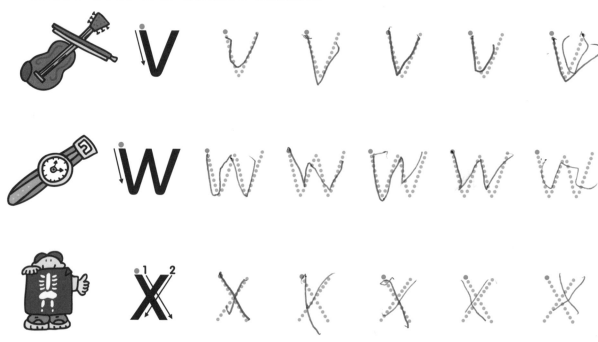

Trace the letters to complete the words.

Violin

X-ray

Watch

Note for parent: This activity helps children to write the letters v, w, x, z, e and s.

Trace over the dotted letters.

 Z z z z z z

 e e e e e e

 s s s s s s

Draw lines to join the pictures that start in the same way.

Capital letters

Capital letters are used at the beginning of names and other important words.
Trace over the dotted lines to make the letters.

N O P Q R S T

N O P Q R S T

U V W X Y Z

U V W X Y Z

Writing names

All names begin with a capital letter.
Write the names and colour the pictures.
Draw a picture of yourself and write your name.

Mummy

Daddy

Granny

Isabella

Note for parent: This activity helps children to learn that names begin with a capital letter.

Matching letters

Trace over the dotted letters. Draw lines to join each letter to a picture that begins with the same letter.

Note for parent: This activity gives practice in writing and matching letters.

Big and little

Look at the pictures.
Put a tick by the things that are little.

Note for parent: Describing and comparing things starts
your child's mathematical development.

Draw a ring around the things that are big.

In, on, under

Can you see where the wolf is hiding?
Draw lines to join the pictures to the right words.

in   on   under

Note for parent: Using positional words such as in, on, under, beside and behind develops awareness of space and movement.

Draw a ball on the chair.

Draw a ball under
the table.

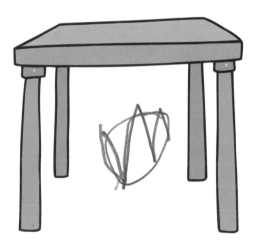

Draw a ball in the box.

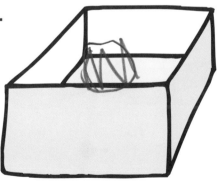

Long, short and tall

Trace the snakes with your finger.
Put a cross by the short snake. Say its colour.
Put a tick by the long snake. Say its colour.

 Note for parent: Use words such as longer, taller, longest and tallest when talking about length and height comparisons.

Look at the giraffes. Put a tick by the short giraffe.
Put a cross by the tall giraffe.

Draw lines to join each giraffe to its tree.

Heavy and light

Draw rings around the things that are heavy.

Note for parent: These activities introduce simple ideas of weight and capacity.

Full or empty?

Look at the pictures. Draw a ring around the things that are empty.

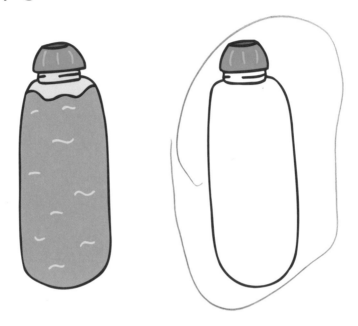

Colour water in the empty bottle and in the empty bath to fill them.

 Note for parent: Experiment with filling and emptying plastic containers at bath time.

Three bears

Draw lines to join each bear to the correct chair.

Draw lines to join each bear to the correct bowl.

Note for parent: Sequencing and matching are important number skills.

Draw lines to join each bear to the correct spoon.

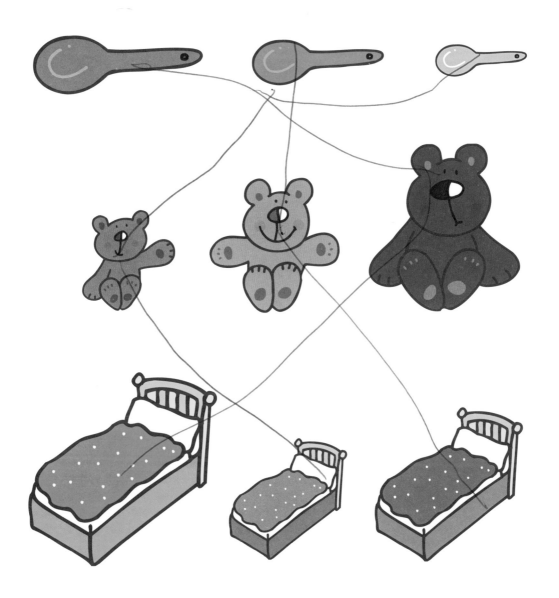

Draw lines to join each bear to the correct bed.

How many?

Draw rings around the correct numbers.

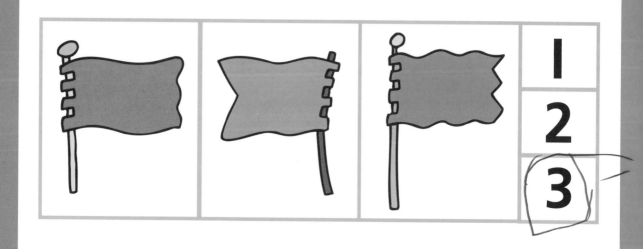

Note for parent: This page shows the numbers 1, 2 and 3 and helps your child to start counting.

One, two, three

Draw dots to match the numbers.

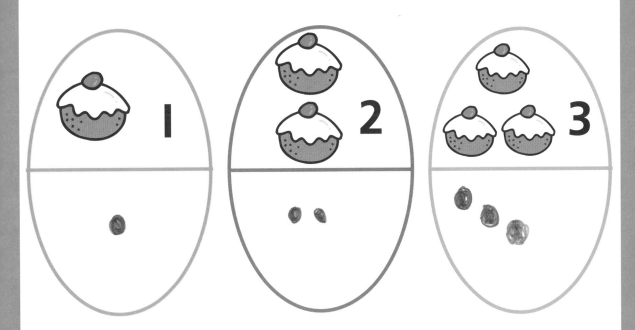

Write in the missing number.

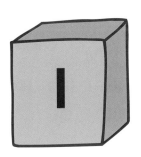

 Note for parent: This page shows the numbers 1, 2 and 3 in different ways.

Counting

Count the candles on each cake.

How old are you? Draw a ring around the cake you had on your birthday. Write your age in the box.

Note for parent: Point to real objects or pictures as you practise counting, don't just recite the words.

Count the animals in each set and draw lines to join each set to the correct number.

1

2

3

4

5

Circles

Trace the circles with your finger.
Which circle is small? Which circle is big?

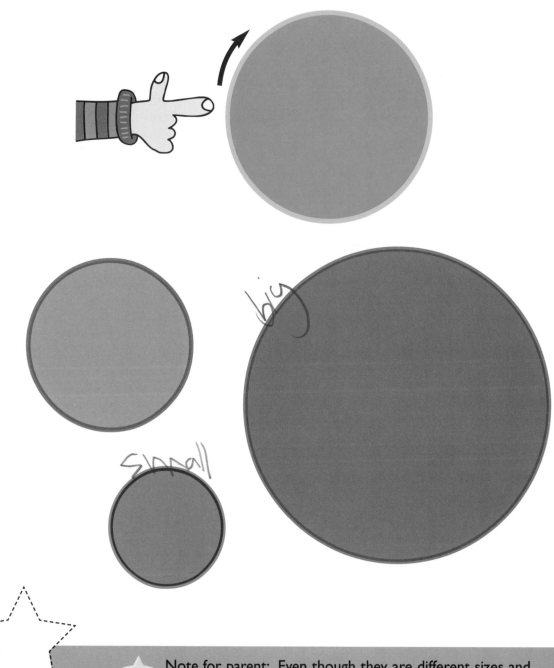

big

small

Note for parent: Even though they are different sizes and
colours, all the circles are the same shape.

Look at the picture and find the circles.
Colour them in.

Triangles

Trace the triangle with your finger.

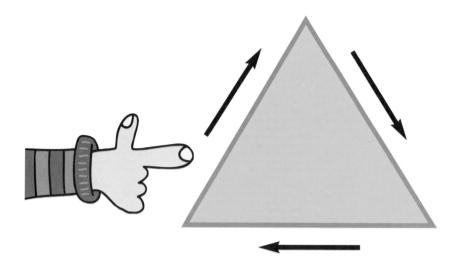

Count the sides – 1, 2, 3. Trace over the dotted lines to complete each triangle.

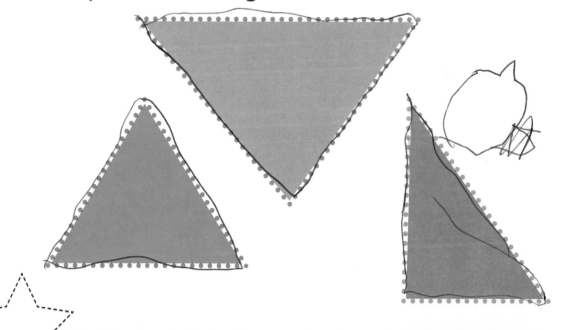

Note for parent: All triangles have three sides.

Look at the picture and find the triangles.
Colour them in.

Squares

Trace the square with your finger.
Count the sides – **1, 2, 3, 4.**

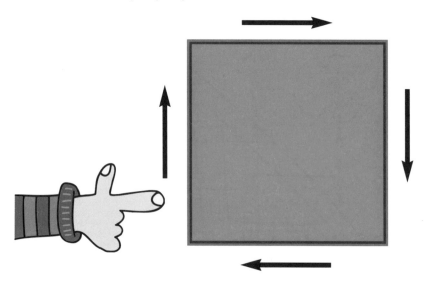

Trace over the dotted lines to finish the squares.
Colour the big square red. Colour the small
square blue.

Note for parent: Squares have four equal sides.

Find the squares in this picture.
Colour them in.

Shapes and colours

Look at the pictures. Name each shape and say its colour.

square

circle

triangle

Colour the shapes on these flags to match the ones above.

Note for parent: Knowing about colours and shapes helps children to sort and match.

Match the shapes

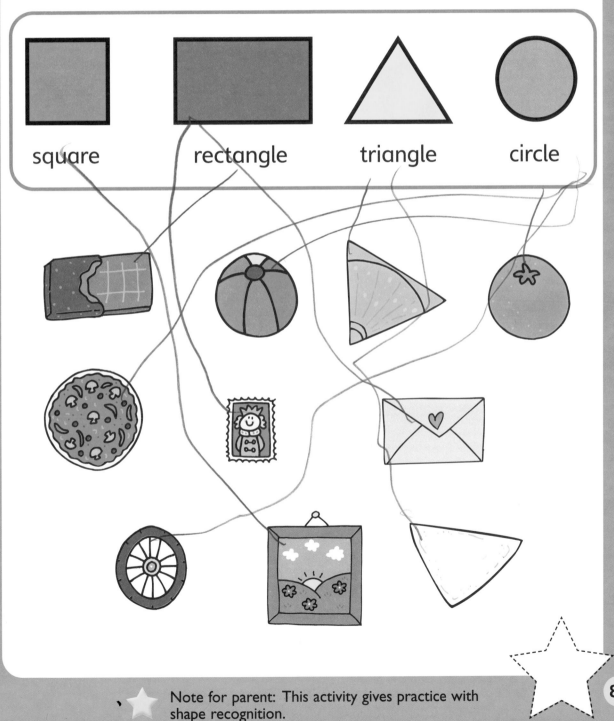

Join each object to its shape.

square   rectangle   triangle   circle

Shape fun

Two tractors need new wheels. Draw lines to join the best wheel for each tractor.

 Note for parent: This activity gives further practice with shape and colour recognition.

Draw lines to join the lollies that are the same.

Four, five, six

Draw the correct number of dots below each set.

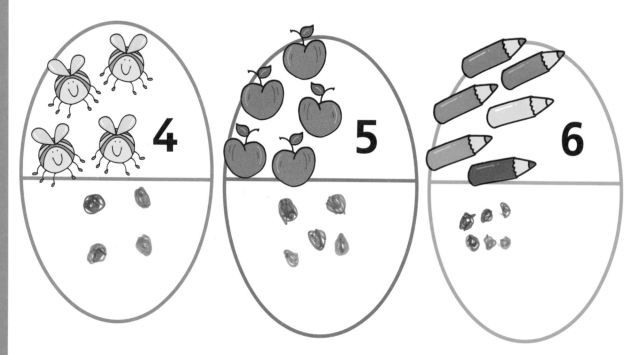

How many candles are on the cake?
Draw a ring around the correct number.

4

5

6

Note for parent: These activities help make the links between the
number word you say, the number symbol and a number of things.

Count the bricks in each set.
Draw lines to join them to the right numbers.

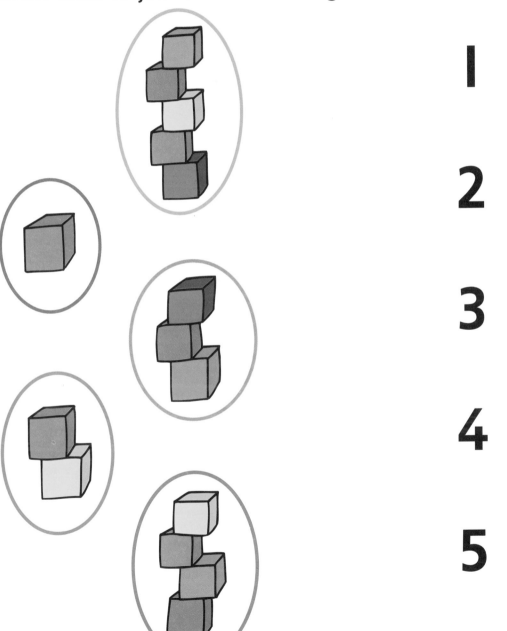

1

2

3

4

5

Up and down

Count up the number stairs.
Count back down again.

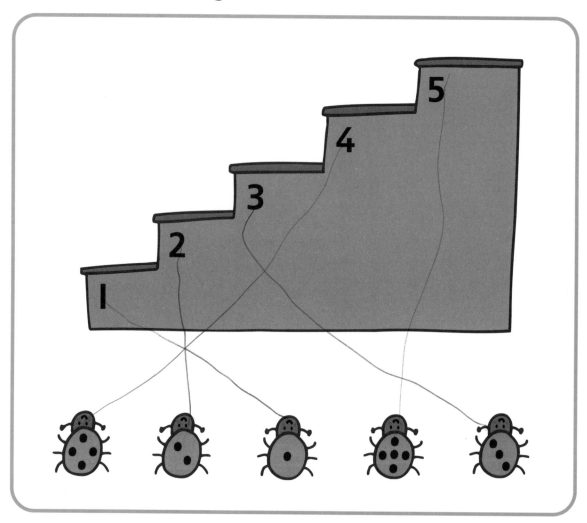

Count the ladybirds' spots.
Draw lines to join each ladybird to the right step.

Note for parent: When your child can count five objects
confidently, then begin to count to ten. Count down as well as up.

Fill in the missing numbers on the ladder.

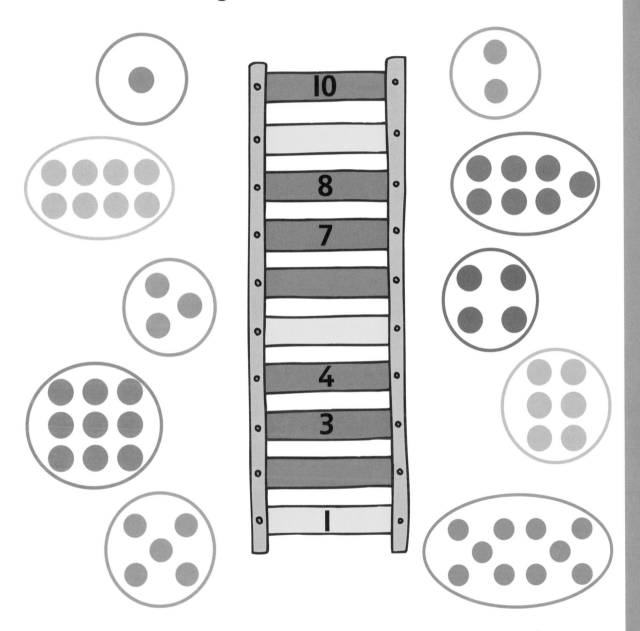

Draw lines to join the dots to the right numbers.

Letter sounds **a–m**

Trace each letter. Draw a ring around two pictures in each row that begin with the same sound.

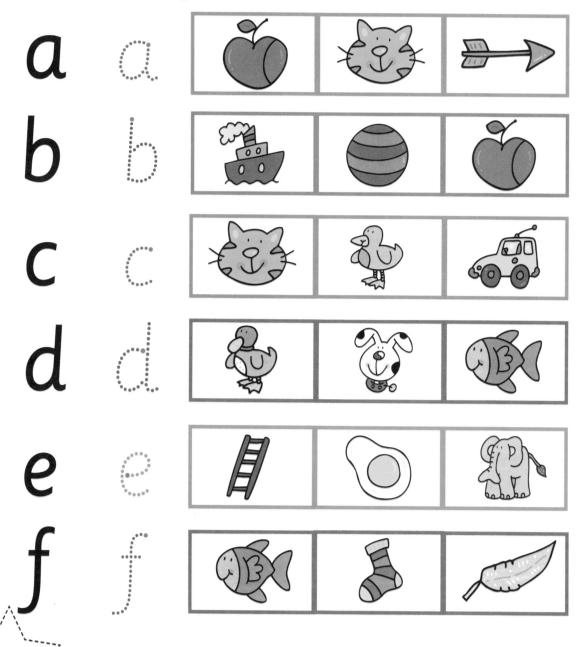

g

h

i

j

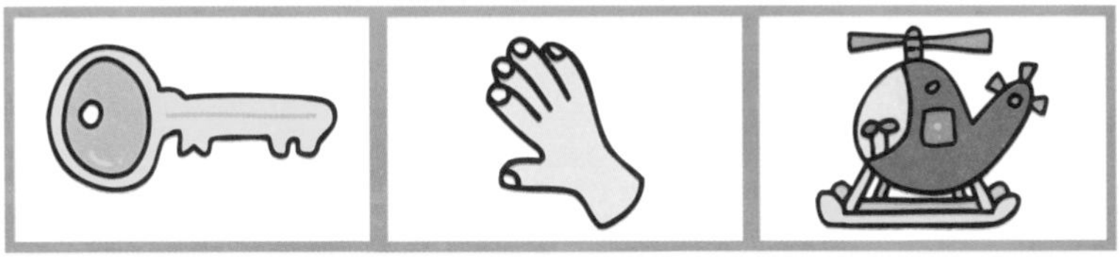

k

l

m

g

h

i

j

k

l

m

Letter sounds n–z

Trace each letter. Draw a ring around two pictures in each row that begin with the same sound.

Note for parent: This activity helps children to understand beginning sounds and to write them.

t t

u u

v v

w w

x x

y y

z z

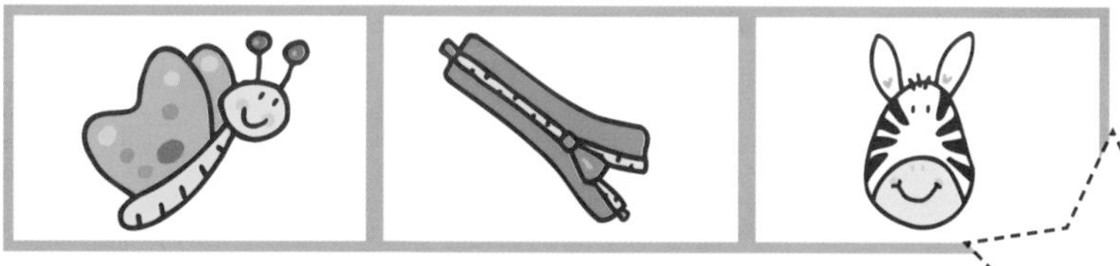

Alphabetical order

Join the letters of the alphabet to make these pictures.

a b c d e f g

h i j k l m n

Note for parent: This activity helps to teach alphabetical order.

o p q r s t

u v w x y z

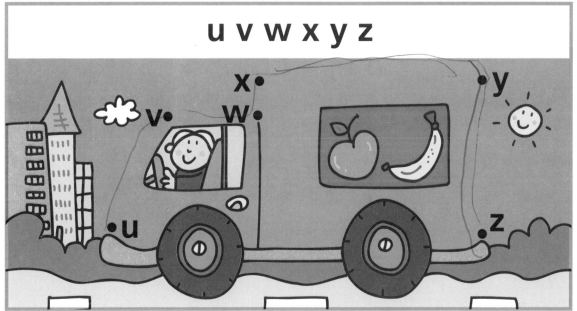

99

Find the pictures

Say the sound of each letter. Look at the big picture and name something beginning with each sound.

d b h k
c a s f

Note for parent: This activity helps children to learn the beginning sounds a, b, c, d, f, h, k and s.

Which letter?

Look at each picture. Choose the right letter and write it in the space to complete each word.

m  o __m__ an	n 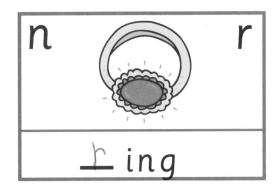 r __r__ ing
s  p __p__ ig	e 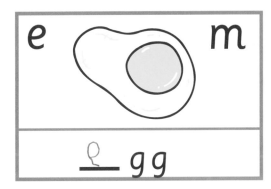 m __e__ gg
g  p __g__ ate	h  l __l__ og

 Note for parent: This activity helps children to learn the beginning sounds e, g, l, m, p and r.

Capital letters

Trace each capital letter and write the matching small one beside it. The first one has been done for you.

A	B	C	D	E	F	G	H	I	J	K	L	M
a	b	c	d	e	f	g	h	i	j	k	l	m

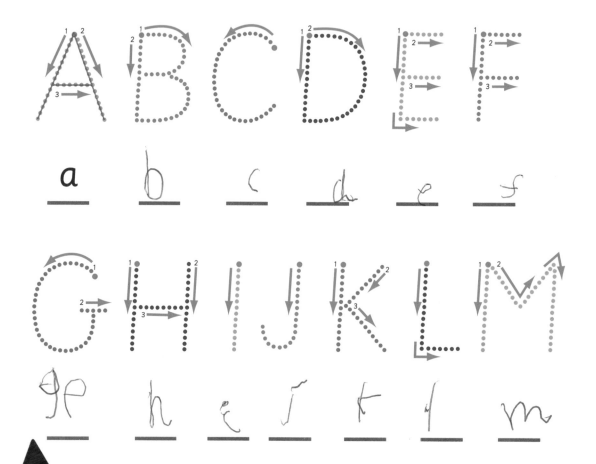

Note for parent: This activity helps children to recognize and write capital letters.

N O P Q R S T U V W X Y Z
n o p q r s t u v w x y z

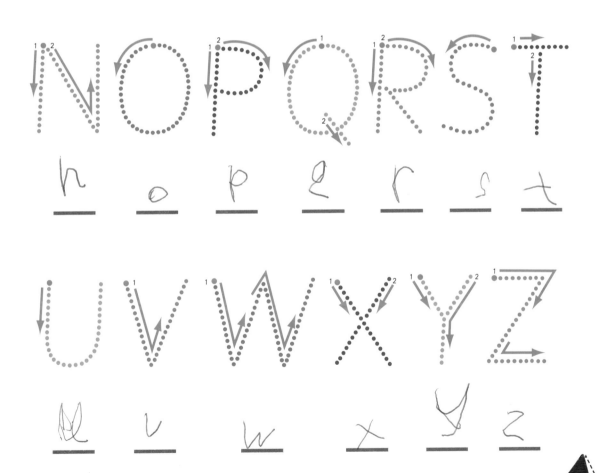

103

Beginning sounds

Say the sound of each letter. Look at the big picture and name something beginning with each sound.

n z t f
w o v k

Note for parent: This activity helps children to learn the beginning sounds f, k, n, o, t, v, w and z.

Second chance

Draw lines to join two pictures to each letter.

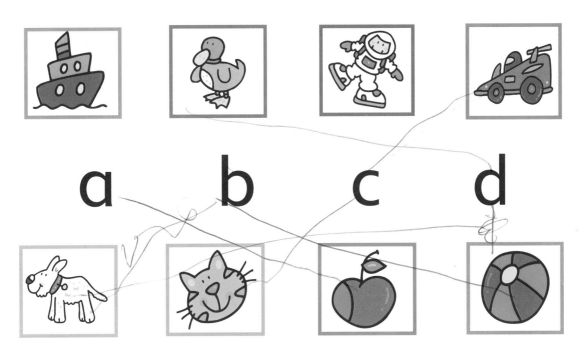

Write the capital letters.

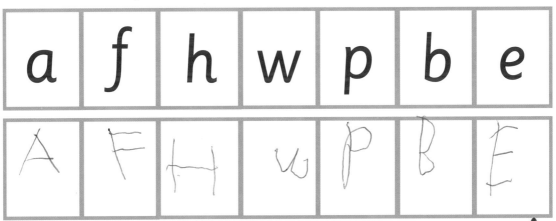

Note for parent: This page gives a chance to see what children can remember from earlier pages.

Begins the same

Say the name of the picture in the middle of each box.
Draw lines to join each middle picture to other pictures
in the box that begin the same way.

 Note for parent: This activity encourages children to speak clearly.

Choose a letter

Choose the right letter from the boxes below to complete each word.

f	h	t	b	k	z

__f__ i s h

__b__ i r d

__h__ a t

__k__ i n g

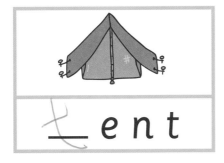

__t__ e n t

__z__ e b r a

107

Note for parent: This activity helps children to recognize the beginning sounds b, f, h, k, t and z.

Find a rhyme

Draw lines to join the pictures that rhyme.

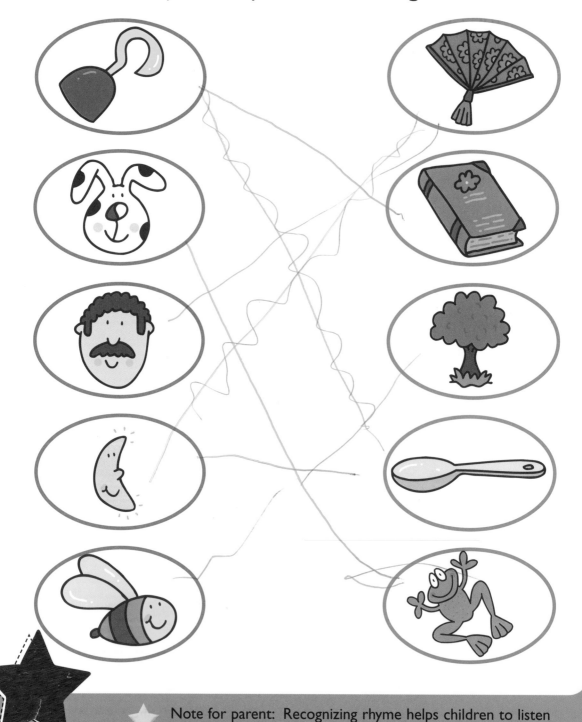

Note for parent: Recognizing rhyme helps children to listen carefully.

In the same way

Say the name of the picture in the middle of each box. Draw lines to join each middle picture to other pictures that begin in the same way.

Note for parent: This activity encourages children to speak clearly.

Learning **b** and **d**

Trace over the letters.

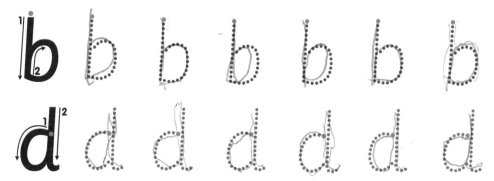

b b b b b b b

d d d d d d d

Choose the letter **b** or **d** to complete the words below.

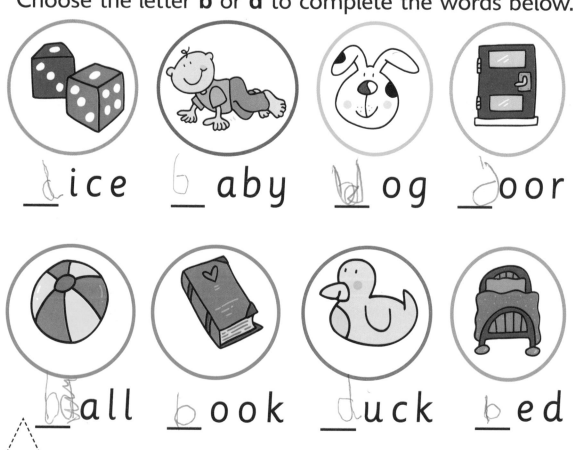

__d__ice __b__ aby __b__ og __d__ oor

__b__all __b__ook __d__uck __b__ ed

Note for parent: Children often confuse the letters b and d. This
activity will help them to learn the difference between the two.

Sound the same

Draw lines to join the pictures that begin in the same way.

Note for parent: This activity encourages children to speak clearly.

Odd one out

Cross out the odd picture inside each shape.

Note for parent: This activity helps children to recognize differences between beginning sounds.

More than one

Write the missing word. Remember to add the letter **s** at the end because there is more than one object.

hat   _ _ _ _

sock   _ _ _ _ _

bat   _ _ _ _

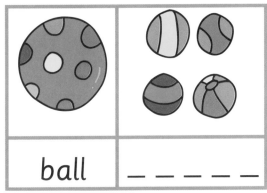

ball   _ _ _ _ _

tree   _ _ _ _ _

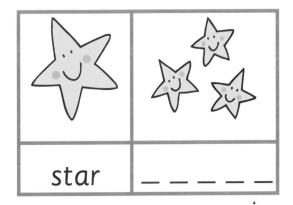

star   _ _ _ _ _

Word endings

Say the name of each picture. Draw a ring around the correct letter that comes at the end of each word.

d   f
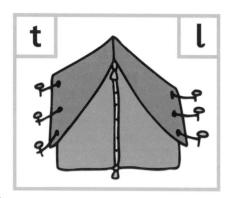

y   g

n   m

k   h

t   l

c   s

Note to parent: This activity encourages children to listen carefully to sounds at the end of words.

Do they rhyme?

Do these pictures rhyme? Put a ✔ or a ✗ in the box under each pair of pictures.

Note for parent: Recognizing rhymes develops good listening skills.

Finding words

Read the words under the pictures. Find the correct letters in the row of mixed-up letters and draw a ring around each one. Write the words in the spaces.

owl

a m b o j s r w c l

_ _ _

moon

b c m s r o t t o n

_ _ _ _

cow

a z c m s o g k w y

_ _ _

drum

e n d y r m r n u m

_ _ _ _

Note for parent: This activity helps children to recognize the letters that make an individual word.

Second chance

Draw lines to join the pictures that rhyme.

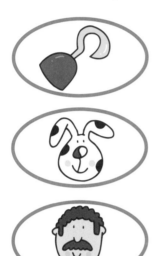 

Cross out the picture in each row that does not belong.

Draw a ring around the letter that comes at the end of each word.

d   f

y   g

 Note for parent: This page tests what children
remember from earlier pages.

Sounds in the middle

Trace over the letters. Say the sounds.

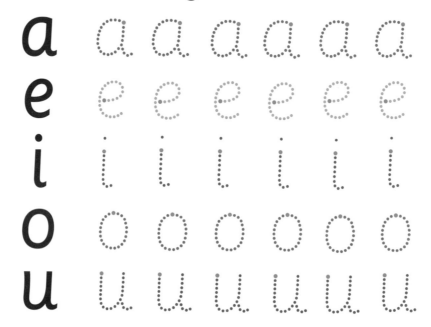

Name each picture. Tick the words with an **a** sound in the middle.

Name each picture. Tick the words with an **e** sound in the middle.

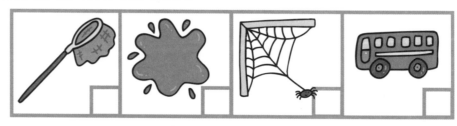

Note to parent: This activity helps children to identify the vowels a, e, i, o and u.

Name each picture. Tick the words with
an **i** sound in the middle.

Name each picture. Tick the words with
an **o** sound in the middle.

Name each picture. Tick the words with
a **u** sound in the middle.

At the beginning

Look at the pictures. Draw a ring around the correct beginning sound.

b d p

j y p

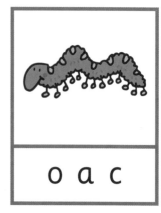

o a c

o a i

d b h

a o c

n u e

h l t

Note for parent: This activity helps children to recognize the letters a, c, d, h, j, o, t and u.

Little words

Find the little words in the grid below.
Draw a ring around each word you find.

so	is	it	on	at
me	go	no	if	we

i	s	b	a	t
w	e	m	e	p
g	h	i	t	v
s	o	r	g	o
w	q	o	n	x
n	o	p	i	f

Note to parent: This activity encourages careful observation.

Count to 3

How many balloons can you count in each set?

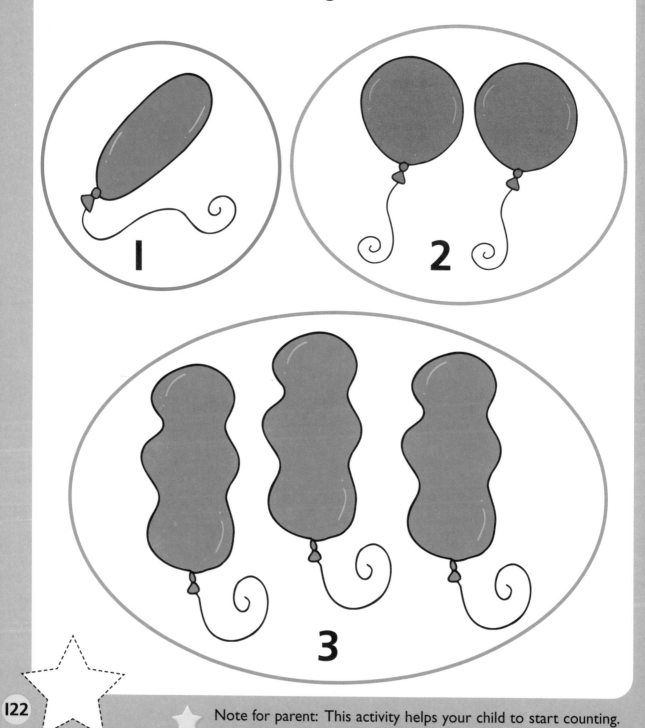

1

2

3

Note for parent: This activity helps your child to start counting.

The same

Count the spots on each shirt. Draw lines to join the T-shirts with the same number of spots.

 Note for parent: Identifying numbers that are the same or different prepares your child for adding and subtracting.

Who has more?

Look at the pictures. Put a tick by the person in each row who has more.

Note for parent: This activity gives more practice in counting from 1 to 3.

Another one

Each dog needs a ball. Draw 1 more.

Each child needs a cake. Draw 1 more.

 Note for parent: Practise making numbers the same when you lay the table or share sweets.

One add one

Point to each picture and count the objects.
Say the numbers out loud.

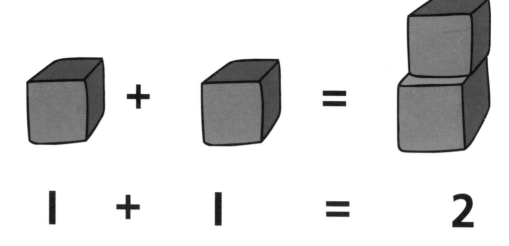

1   +   1   =   2

One and one make two.

1   +   1   =   2

Note for parent: Follow the sums with your finger
as you say them with your child.

Write the numbers in the boxes to make the totals.

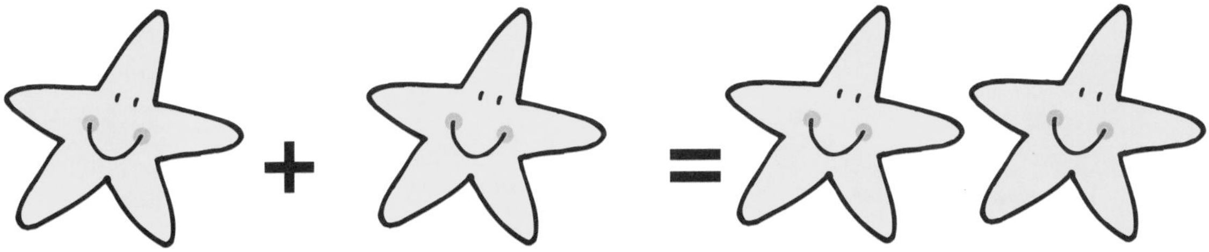

1 + 1 = ☐

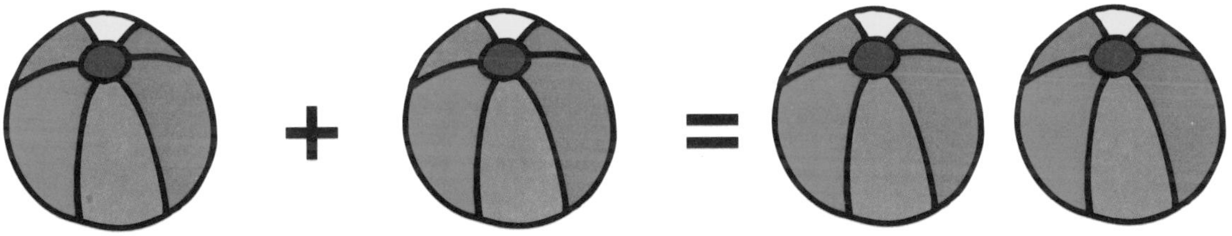

1 + 1 = ☐

Two add one

Point to each picture and count the objects.
Say the numbers out loud.

2   +   1   =   3

Two and one make three.

2   +   1   =   3

Note for parent: Count the things on the left, then the things on
the right. Are the numbers the same?

Colour the answers to these sums.

2 + 1 = 3

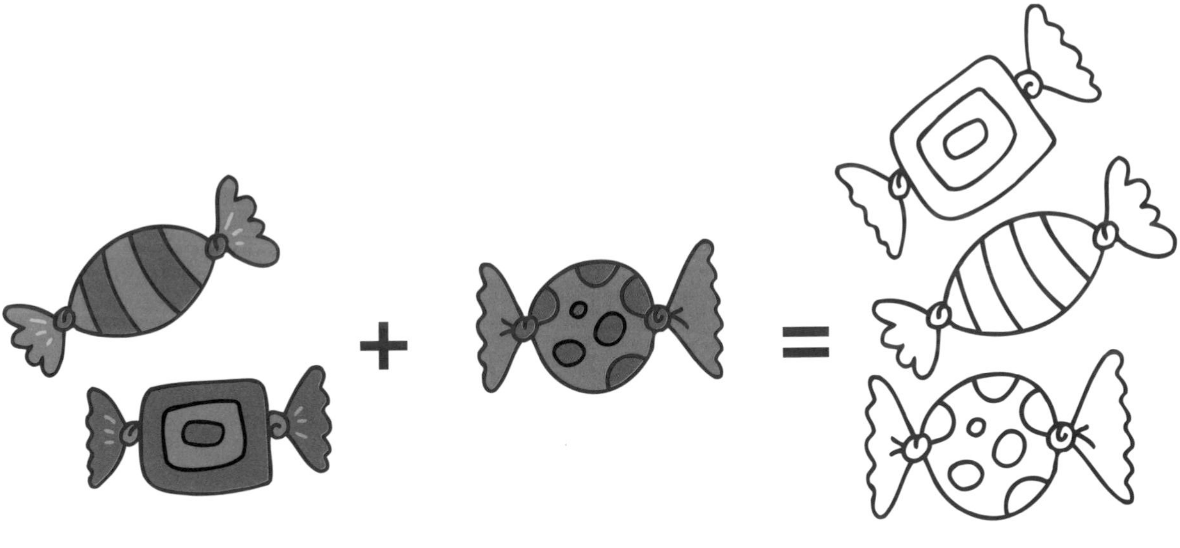

2 + 1 = 3

129

Count 4 and 5

Colour four ducks.

Colour five fish.

Note for parent: Children often find it difficult to count
objects that are not arranged in tidy rows.

The same or more?

Join each rabbit to a hole. Are there more rabbits or holes? Tick the correct box.

more rabbits ☐   more holes ☐

Draw lines to see if there are more dogs or kennels. Tick the correct box.

more kennels ☐   more dogs ☐

 Note for parent: Matching objects one-by-one shows if the numbers are the same or different.

One more

Colour one more flag.

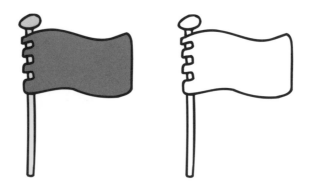

How many flags are there altogether?

Colour one more apple.

How many apples are there altogether?

Note for parent: Use a variety of words to talk about adding —
add, and, plus, make, one more, another one, altogether, sum.

Colour one more butterfly.

How many butterflies are there altogether?

Colour one more hat.

How many hats are there altogether?

Add 1

Point to each picture and count the objects.
Say the numbers out loud.

1 + 1 = 2

One and one make two.

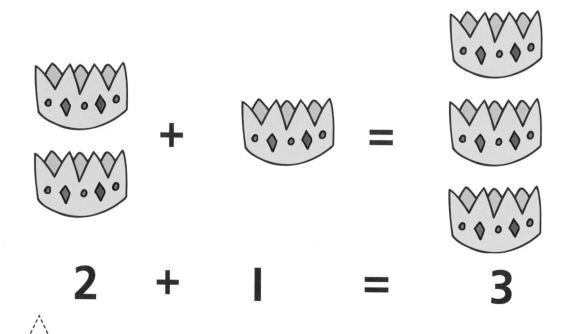

2 + 1 = 3

Note for parent: Point out that the last number in the count
gives the total.

3   +   I   =   4

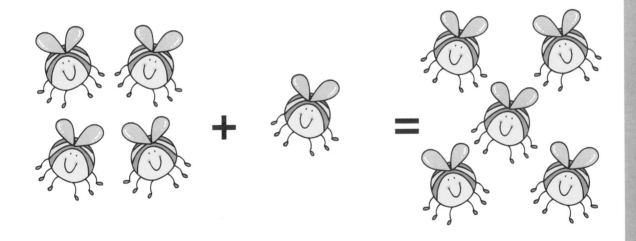

4   +   I   =   5

Two more

Colour two more shells.

How many shells are there altogether?

Colour two more balls.

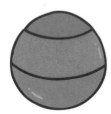 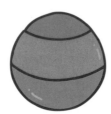  

How many balls are there altogether?

Colour two more presents.

How many presents are there altogether?

 Note for parent: In this activity your child is adding things or objects, rather than numbers.

Add 2

Point to each picture and count the objects.
Say the numbers out loud.

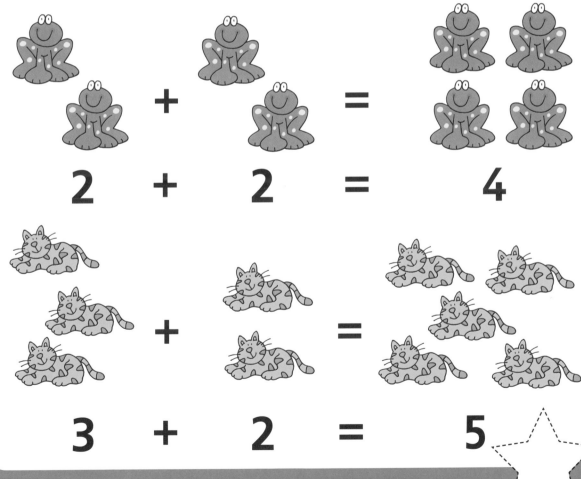

1 + 2 = 3

One and two make three.

2 + 2 = 4

3 + 2 = 5

Note for parent: This activity gives children practice
in adding up to 5.

Three more

Colour three more boats.

How many boats are there altogether?

Colour three more trees.

How many trees are there altogether?

Note for parent: This activity gives further practice with adding.

Add 3

Point to each picture and count the objects.
Say the numbers out loud.

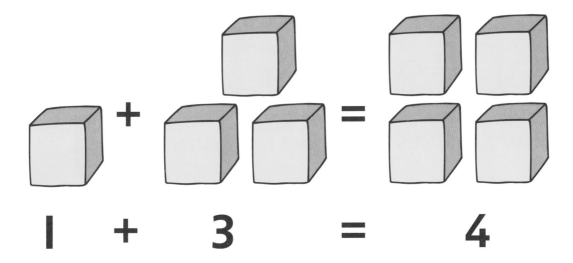

1 + 3 = 4

One and three make four.

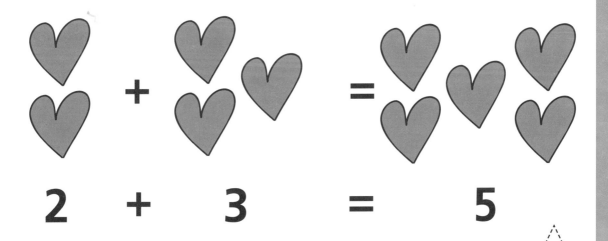

2 + 3 = 5

Note for parent: Building brick towers is an excellent
way to make number work fun.

Four more

Colour four more stars.

How many stars are there altogether?

Colour four more cars.

How many cars are there altogether?

 Note for parent: This activity gives further practice with adding things or objects.

Add 4

Point to each picture and count the objects.
Say the numbers out loud.

1 + 4 = 5

One and four make five.

1 + 4 = 5

Note for parent: Encourage your child to use his or her fingers to count, add and subtract.

More or less?

Look at the pictures. Draw a line to join the two children with the same number of cakes.

Draw a ring around the child with the most cakes.

Note for parent: The idea of 'less' is needed to understand subtraction.

Count the ladybirds' spots.
Tick the ladybird with one less spot.

Count the candles on the cakes.
Tick the cake with one more candle.

Take one away

Point to each picture and count the objects.
Write the missing numbers in the boxes.

5

take one away leaves

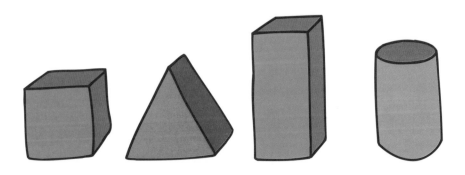

4 take one away leaves

Note for parent: Use real objects to practise taking away.

3   take one away leaves

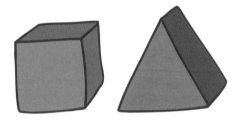

2   take one away leaves

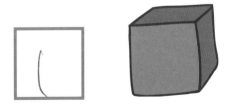

1

How many are left?

Look at the picture. Take two crayons from the box.
How many are left? Draw the answer in the box.

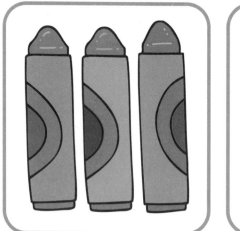

Burst two balloons. How many are left?
Draw the answer in the box.

Note for parent: Activities such as these introduce your child
to subtraction in a practical way.

Look at the picture. Pick three apples.
How many are left on the tree?
Colour them. Write your answer in the box.

Take four cakes. How many are left?
Colour it in. Write your answer in the box.

Five little ducks

Point to each picture and count the objects.
Write the missing numbers in the boxes.

5

Five little ducks went swimming one day,
Over the pond and far away.
Mother Duck said quack, quack, quack,
But only four little ducks came back.

Four little ducks...

 Note for parent: This activity gives further practice in counting to 5.

Three little ducks...

Two little ducks...

One little duck...

149

The alphabet **a–m**

Trace the letters. Say the sound that each letter makes. The pictures will help you.

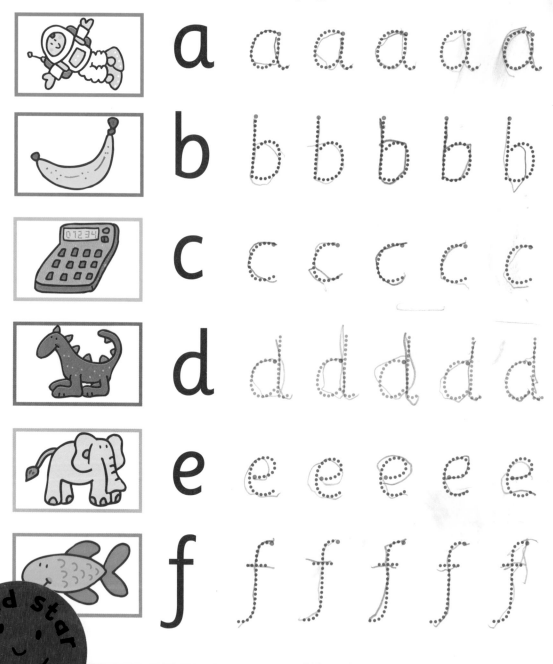

a   a a a a a a

b   b b b b b

c   c c c c c c

d   d d d d d d

e   e e e e e e

f   f f f f f

Note for parent: It is very important to know the letters of the alphabet and the sounds they make.

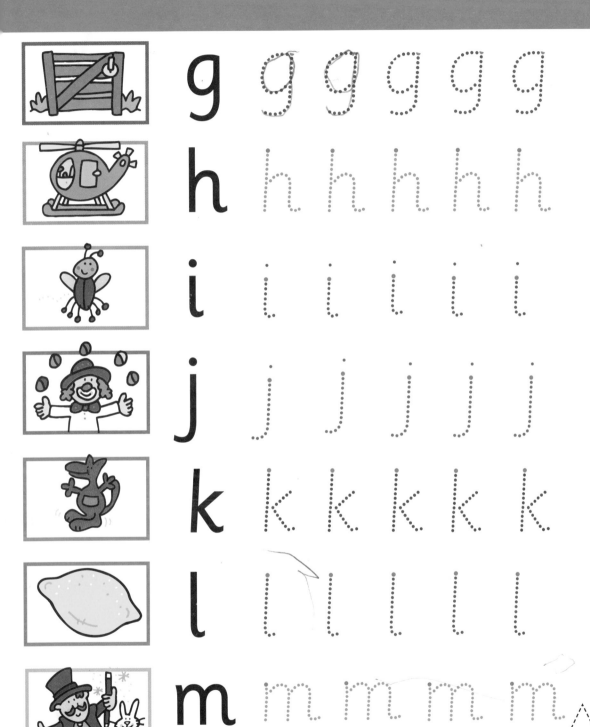

g g g g g g

h h h h h h

i i i i i i

j j j j j j

k k k k k k

l l l l l l

m m m m m m

The alphabet **n–z**

Trace the letters. Say the sound that each letter makes. The pictures will help you.

n   n   n   n   n   n   n

o   o   o   o   o   o   o

p   p   p   p   p   p   p

q   q   q   q   q   q   q

r   r   r   r   r   r   r

s   s   s   s   s   s   s

Note for parent: It is very important to know the letters of the alphabet and the sounds they make.

 t t t t t t

 u u u u u u

 v v v v v v

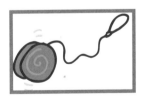 w w w w w w

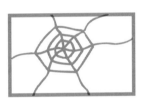 x x x x x x

 y y y y y y

 z z z z z z

Sounds the same

Draw lines to join the pictures that start in the same way. The first one has been done for you.

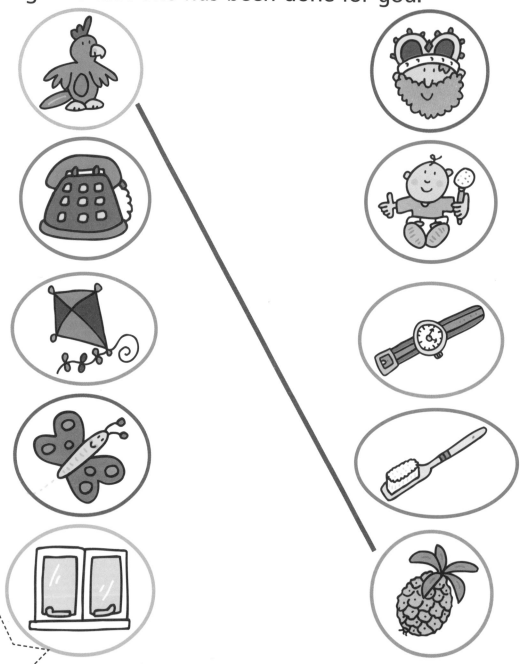

Note for parent: This activity helps children to recognize the beginning sounds b, k, p, t and w.

Odd one out

Cross out the one that does not belong in each row.

 Note for parent: This activity helps children to recognize the beginning sounds d, j, k, m and z.

Find the letters

Trace the lines to join each child to a fish.
Write the correct letter below each child's face.

These letters make a word. Can you read it?

156

Note for parent: This activity helps with word building using the letters f, h, i and s.

Rhyme time

Say the name of each picture. Put a cross over the odd one out in each row.

 Note to parent: Recognizing rhyme helps children to listen carefully.

Find the pictures

Write the beginning sound for each animal in the correct box.

Can you find something in the picture that begins in the same way as [sheep] ?

Can you find something in the picture that begins in the same way as [chick] ?

Note for parent: This activity encourages children to listen to beginning sounds and then write them.

Writing letters

Say the name of each picture and write its beginning letter.

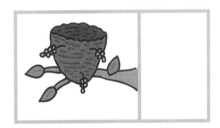

Note for parent: This activity gives practice in writing the letters a, c, d, j, l, n, r, s, t and v.

Find the rhymes

Colour the pictures that rhyme with Pat.

Write the correct letter to complete each word.

C a t   R a t   H a t   b a t

Note for parent: This activity gives practice in finding rhymes and writing the beginning letters b, c, h and r.

Right or wrong?

Put a tick or a cross in each box: yes ✔ no ✗

begins with f ☐

begins with m ☐

begins with b ☐

begins with d ☐

begins with w ☐

begins with l ☐

Note for parent: This activity encourages children to listen carefully to beginning sounds.

161

Word endings

Use the letters from the box below to finish the words.

p   n   d   g   b   w   t   n

c o __

t r a i __

m o __

p i __

c r a __

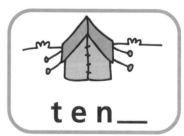

t e n __

s u __

b i r __

 Note for parent: Word endings are difficult and need lots of practice.

Second chance

Draw lines to join the pictures that start in the same way.

Say each word and write the beginning letter.

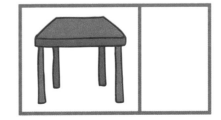

Note for parent: This page is a chance to see what children have remembered.

Words inside

Find another word inside each big word. Write the small word. Then draw a picture of it.

snail

donkey

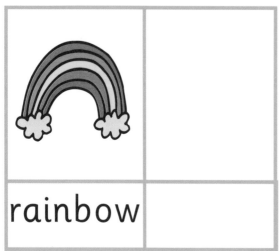

rainbow

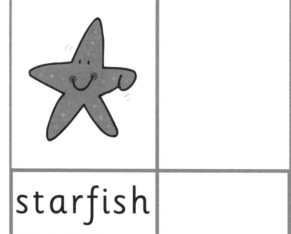

starfish

Note to parent: Children enjoy discovering words within words.

Middle letters

Draw a ring around the correct word beside
each picture.

 **dog / dig**    **mup / mop**

 **hat / hot**    **bas / bus**

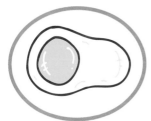 **egg / igg**    **cup / cap**

 **pig / pog**    **san / sun**

 Note for parent: This activity helps children to
recognize short vowels in the middle of words.

Double sounds

Draw lines to join two pictures that start in the same way. There are five picture pairs altogether.

Note for parent: This activity gives further practice with the double sounds ch and sh.

Write **ch** or **sh** to finish the words.

 _ _ a i r

 _ _ e e p

 _ _ o e s

 _ _ u r c h

 _ _ i c k

Learn about **th**

Trace over the letters. Write **th** at the beginning of each word. Now read the completed words.

__ __ r o n e

__ __ i r t e e n

__ __ r e e

__ __ e r m o m e t e r

Can you think of another word that begins with **th**? You have one on each hand.

 Note to parent: This activity helps children to understand the double sound th.

Crossword

Look at the pictures and complete the crossword.

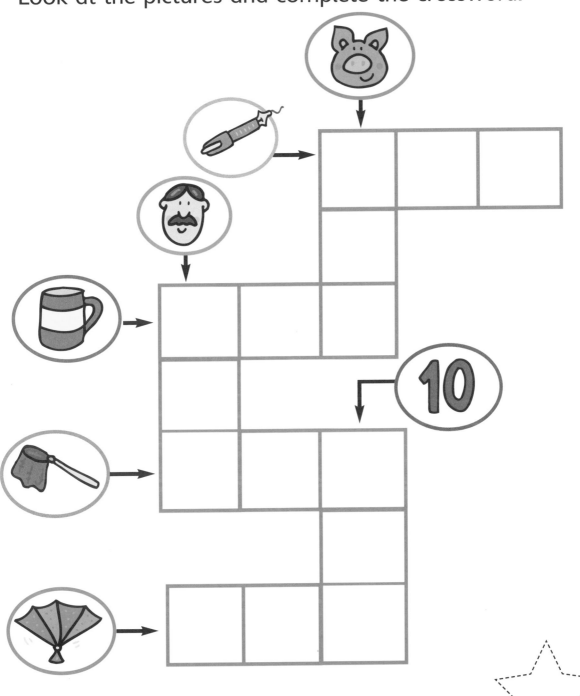

Note for parent: This crossword helps with simple spelling.

Animal letters

Look at the letters. Say each sound.
Join each letter to an animal in the big picture that begins with the same sound.

z　c　e　m

p　l　t　k

Note to parent: This activity helps children to identify
the initial sounds c, e, k, l, m, p, t and z.

Last letters

Say the name of each picture. Tick the correct letter at the end of each word.

p

d

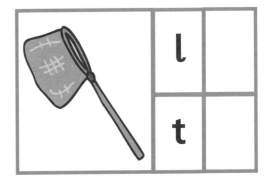

l

t

p

g

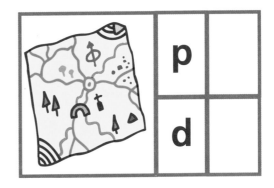

p

d

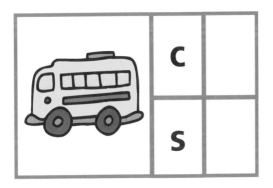

c

s

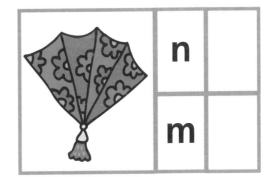

n

m

171

Note to parent: This activity gives practice with the final consonant sounds g, n, p, s and t.

Three-letter words

Say the name of each picture. Find the words in the grid and circle them. Remember to look across and down.

c	o	w	d	i	m
j	r	b	a	t	l
w	s	u	n	f	j
z	i	s	p	k	u
y	x	v	e	g	g
h	q	t	g	n	p

Note for parent: This activity gives practice in spelling short words.

Adding final s

You add the letter **s** at the end of a word when there is more than one item.

 sock

 socks

Complete these words.

 = shoe

 = _ _ _ _ _

 = hat

 = _ _ _ _

 = glove

 = _ _ _ _ _ _

 = coat

 = _ _ _ _ _

Note for parent: This activity helps children to understand plurals.

Second chance

Write **ch** or **sh** to finish the words.

_ _ a i r   _ _ e e p   _ _ o e s

Draw a ring around the correct word.

 dog / dig    mup / mop

 hat / hot    bas / bus

Tick the correct letter at the end of each word.

p	✓
d	

l	
t	✓

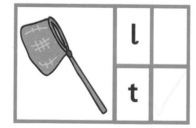

p	
g	✓

p	
d	

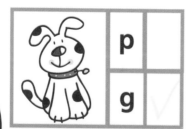
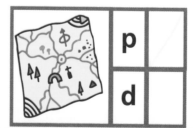

I am the best!

More double sounds

Write **sh**, **ch** or **th** at the beginning or the end of these words.

_ _ o e s

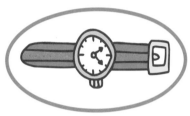

w a t _ _

b r u _ _

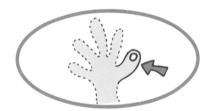

_ _ u m b

_ _ a i r

t o o _ _

Put a cross over the odd one out.

Note for parent: This activity gives more practice with the double-letter sounds sh, ch and th.

Check your spelling

Look at the pictures. Cross out the words that are spelled incorrectly.

 **ball**

bell

 **hut**

hat

 **fox**

fos

 **pin**

pen

 **kat**

cat

 **man**

men

Can you spell these words?

 p i g

_ _ _

 k i t

_ _ _

  Note to parent: This activity gives practice with simple spellings.

Picture quiz

Look carefully at the picture. Ask an adult to read the questions.

What begins with each of these letters: **b**, **c**, **d** and **n**?
What ends with the letters **d**, **g**, **k** and **t**?
What begins with the double letters **ch**, **sh** and **th**?

Note to parent: This activity helps children to remember sounds that they have learned earlier.

Drawing shapes

Trace over the dotted lines to make the shapes.
Read the name of each shape.

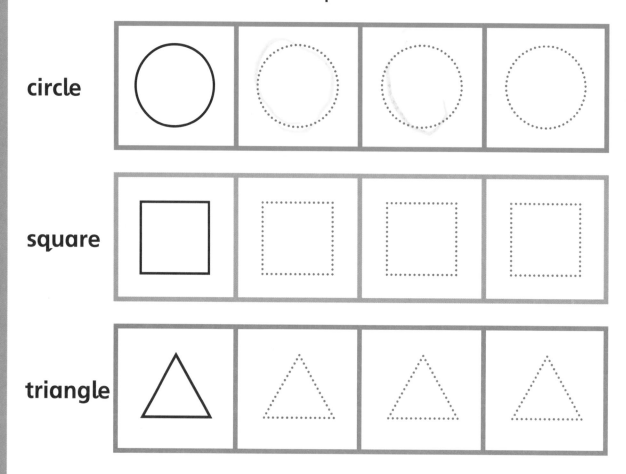

circle

square

triangle

Read the words and draw each shape.

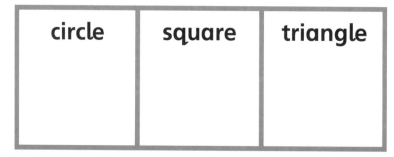

circle	square	triangle

 Note for parent: This activity helps children
to draw simple shapes.

rectangle

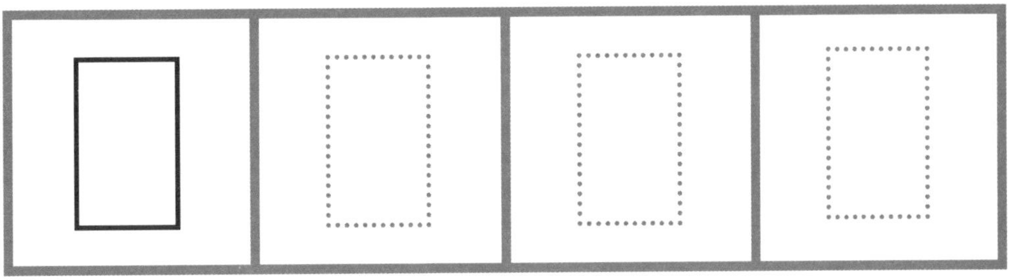

diamond

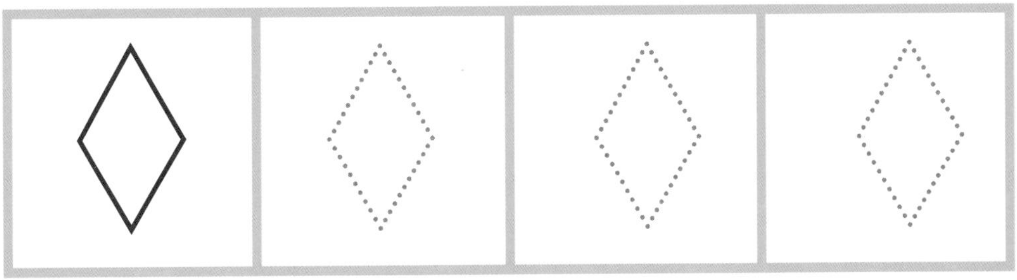

oval

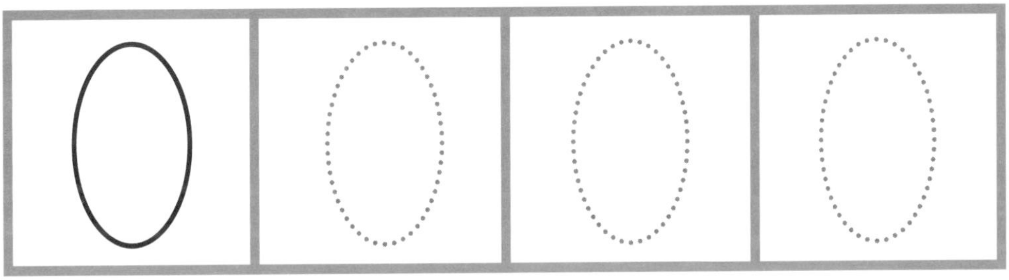

Read the words and draw each shape.

rectangle	diamond	oval

Read and colour

Read the words. Colour the balloons to match.

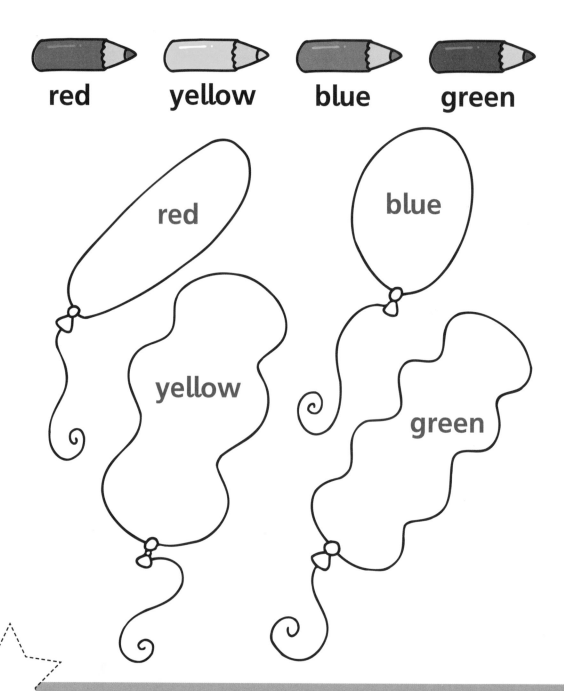

red　　yellow　　blue　　green

red

blue

yellow

green

Note for parent: This activity helps children to recognize colours.

Read the words. Colour the kite.
Choose your own colours for the tail.

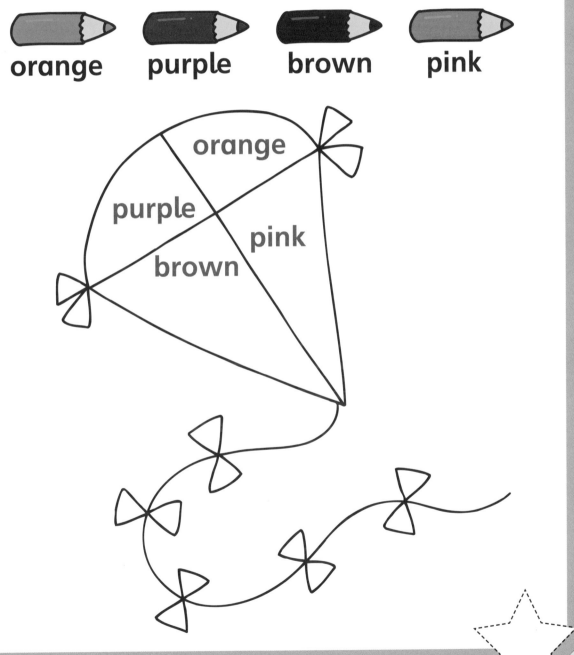

orange   purple   brown   pink

orange
purple
pink
brown

Find the shapes

Look at the shapes below. Find them in the big picture and colour them.

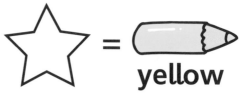

△ = green   ☆ = yellow

Note for parent: This activity helps children to identify shapes and colours.

○ = 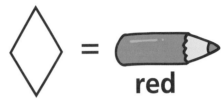 **orange**

◇ = **red**

183

Writing colours

Read the words. Trace each word underneath.

red

red

green

green

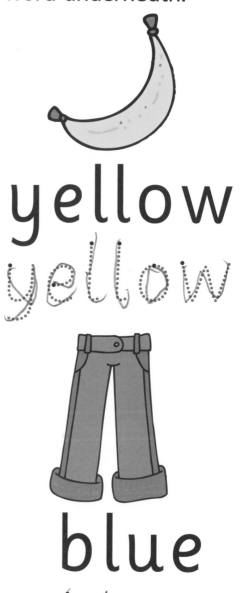

yellow

yellow

blue

blue

Note for parent: This activity helps children practise writing colour names.

More shapes to draw

Look at the shape in the first box and draw another one to match. Say the name of each shape.

Note for parent: This activity gives further practice in drawing shapes.

Matching colours

Colour each balloon to match the child's jumper.

Note for parent: This page helps children with colour matching.

Finding colours

Read the words. Look at the picture. Draw a ring round the colours that are used in the picture.

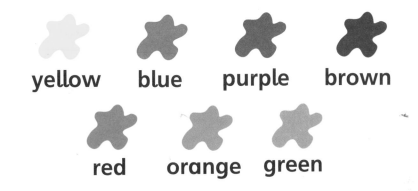

yellow   blue   purple   brown

red   orange   green

 Note for parent: This page helps children to identify colours in pictures.

187

Solid shapes

Join each set of shapes to its name.

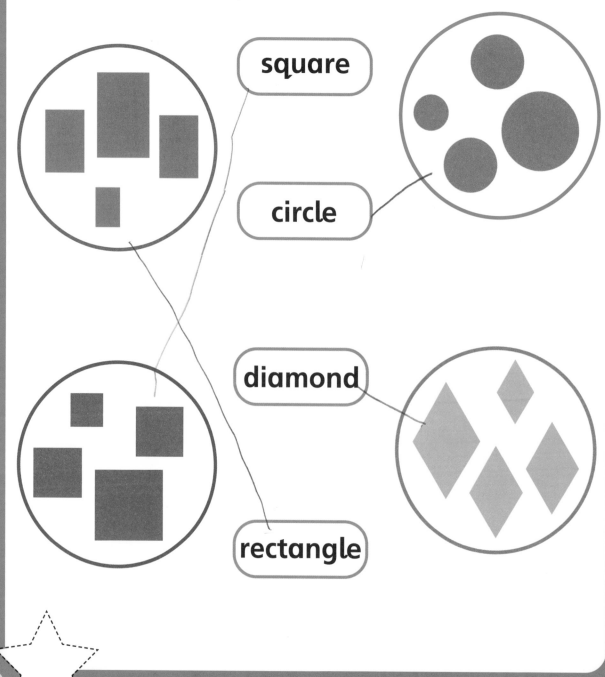

square

circle

diamond

rectangle

Note for parent: Your child will gradually learn the names of common shapes.

Finish the patterns

Draw one more shape in each row to finish the pattern.

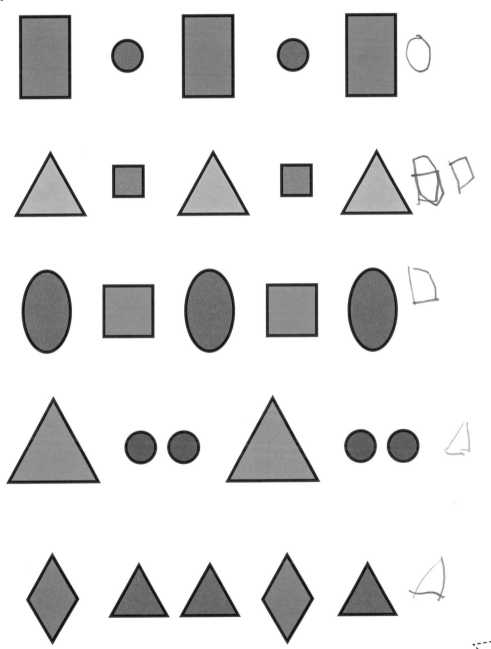

189

Bubble time

How many bubbles can you see?

Write the answer in the box.
Draw 3 more bubbles.

What shape are they? _____

9

Note for parent: This page gives further practice in examining shapes closely.

Basket of fruit

Colour the fruit in the bowl.
Which colours have you used twice?

 Note for parent: This page helps children to learn about colours.

191

Colour code

Read the words. Colour the diamonds using these colours.

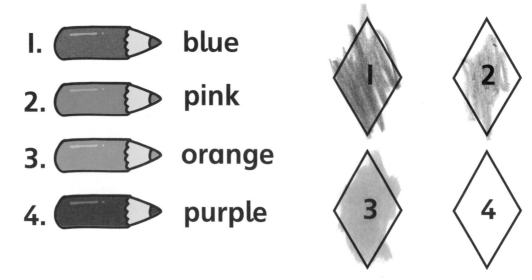

1. blue
2. pink
3. orange
4. purple

Read the words. Colour the squares using these colours.

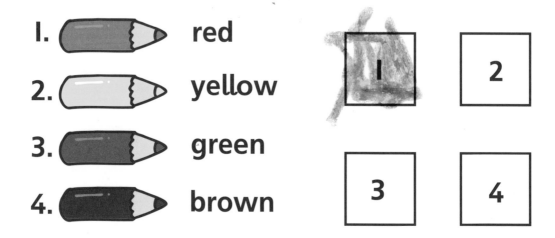

1. red
2. yellow
3. green
4. brown

Note for parent: Careful colouring helps develop manual co-ordination.

Read the words.
Colour the butterfly using these colours.

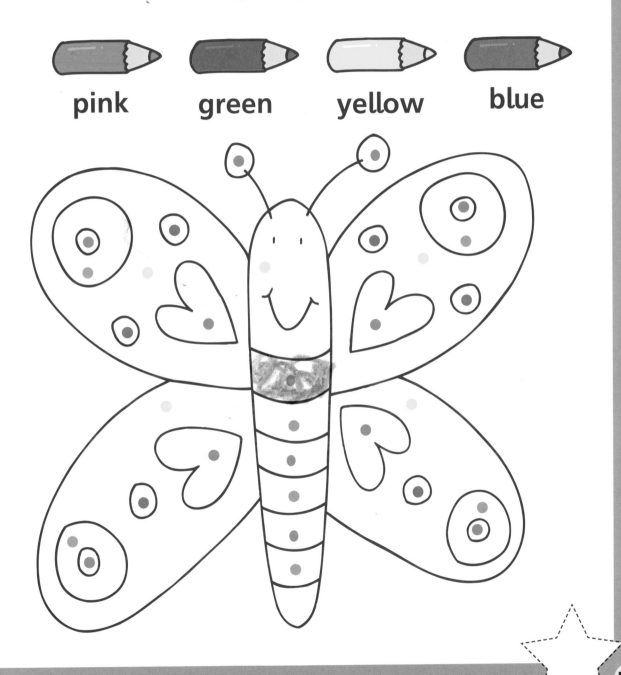

pink   green   yellow   blue

Make two the same

Colour picture 2 to match picture 1.

1.

2.

1.

2.

 Note for parent: This page helps children to match colours.

Colour patterns

Finish the colour patterns.
Say the name of each colour and each shape.

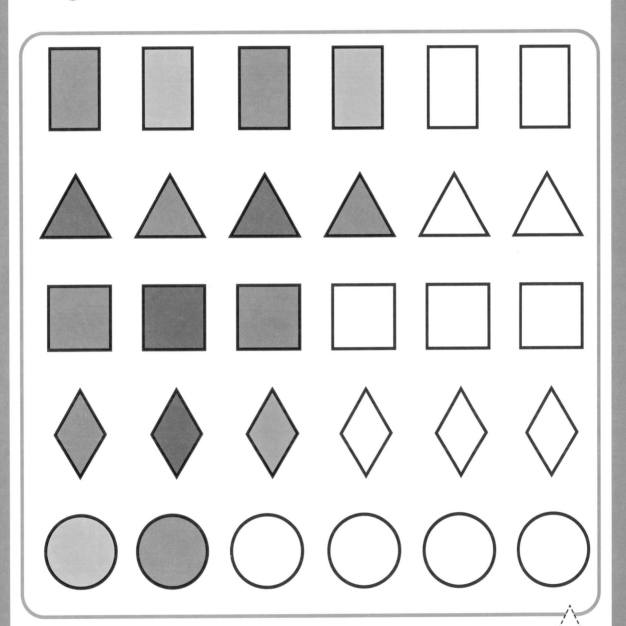

 Note for parent: This page helps children to understand repeat patterns and the names of shapes and colours.

Big and little

Draw lines to join the shapes that are the same.
Colour them in. For each shape use a different colour.

Note for parent: This page gives practice with shape recognition.

Colour the fish

Read the words.
Colour the picture using these colours.

 **green**  **red**  **purple**  **yellow**  **blue**

 Note for parent: This activity gives more practice using specific colours.

Odd one out

Draw a ring around the one that does not belong in each row.

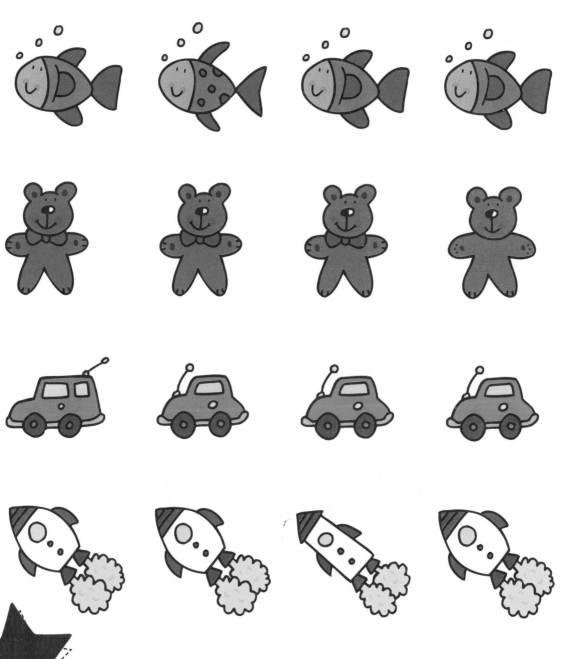

Note for parent: This page encourages careful observation of shapes.

Colour by numbers

Read the words. Colour the picture.
The numbers tell you which colours to use.

green   **red**   **purple**   **yellow**   **orange**

Note for parent: This activity gives further practice using specific colours.

Two the same

Look at the pictures. Colour 2 butterflies that are the same.

Colour 2 parrots that are the same.

Note for parent: This activity helps children observe detailed patterns.

Fitting shapes

Join each shape to its shadow.

Note for parent: Recognizing simple shapes is an
important part of mathematics.

Missing shapes

Look carefully at the pictures. There are 5 shapes missing in the bottom picture.
Draw them and colour the picture.

Note for parent: This activity helps children to find shapes and draw them.

Birthday presents

Draw a line to match each parcel to the correct object.

Note for parent: Recognizing strong shapes is a good start to sorting.

Odd one out

Cross out the odd one out in each box.

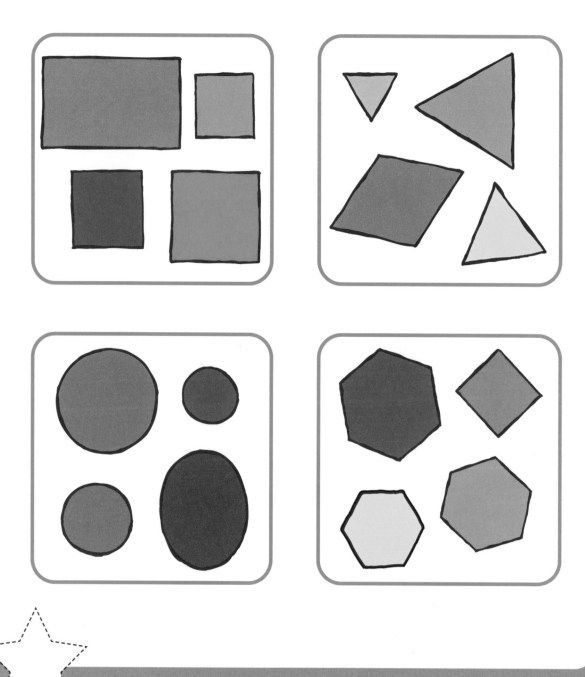

Note for parent: This activity gives further practice with shape recognition.

Can you remember?

Draw a ring around the word 'Yes' or 'No'.

1. This is a square.   Yes   No

2. This is a circle.   Yes   No

3. This is a triangle.   Yes   No

4. This is a circle.   Yes   No

5. This is an oval.   Yes   No

6. This is a rectangle.   Yes   No

7. This is a rectangle.   Yes   No

8. This is a diamond.   Yes   No

 Note for parent: Your child will need help reading these words.

205

Rhyming pictures

Look at the little pictures and read the words. Find something in the big picture that rhymes with each little picture.

wall

bat

mouse

chicks

coat

star

Note for parent: This activity will help children understand rhyming pairs.

Body words

Trace the words in the boxes. Draw lines to join each picture to the right word.

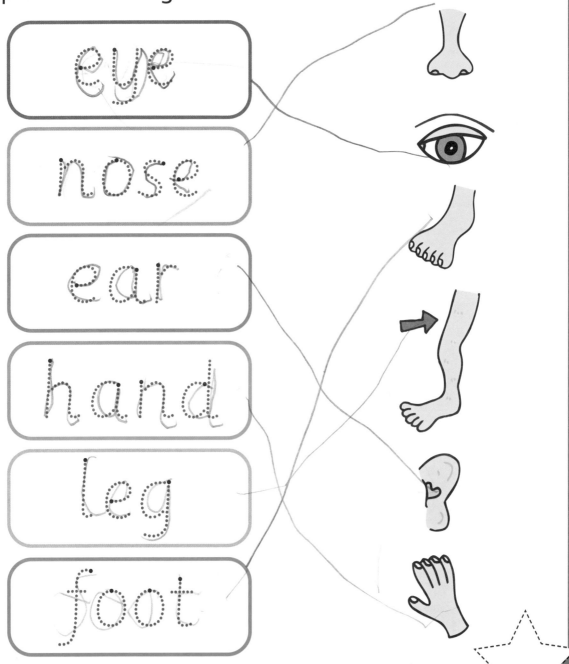

eye

nose

ear

hand

leg

foot

 Note for parent: This activity helps children learn to read and write body words.

207

Odd one out

Name each picture. Draw a ring around the picture in each set that does not rhyme.

Note for parent: This activity encourages children to listen carefully to rhymes.

Rhyming pairs

Draw rings around the two pictures that rhyme in each row.

Note for parent: This activity helps children to identify rhymes.

Fishing fun

What does each bear catch?
Trace the words and read them.

fish

crab

boot

worm

Note for parent: This activity helps children
to practise hand control.

Creepy crawly words

Look for each of the words below in the letter grid. Draw a ring around each one when you find it.

spider   ant   worm   bee

s	p	i	d	e	r
b	t	w	a	h	k
e	l	o	z	b	x
e	c	r	v	n	r
u	p	m	q	e	r
d	a	n	t	a	t

Note for parent: This activity helps children recognize insect words.

In the kitchen

Find all these things below in the big picture.
Write the correct number in each box.

1. kettle
2. pan
3. apron
4. brush
5. toaster
6. iron

Big and little

An elephant  is big.

A mouse is little.

Look at the pictures below. Tick the things that are big.

 ☑

 ☐

 ☐

 ☑

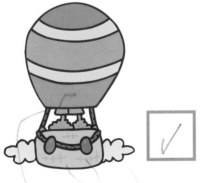 ☑

 ☐

Note for parent: This page shows the concept of big and little.

Nursery rhymes

Read the words.
Draw rings around the words that rhyme.
Finish colouring the pictures.

Little Miss Muffet
Sat on a tuffet.

Hey diddle diddle,
The cat and the
fiddle.

Note for parent: This activity gives children more practice
with rhyming words.

Little Jack Horner
Sat in a corner.

Ring a ring of roses,
A pocket full of
posies.

What sounds?

Trace each word and read it. The pictures will help you.
What sound does each thing or animal make?

bell

cat

duck

owl

dog

drum

Note for parent: This page helps children to connect sounds to pictures and words (meow for cat etc.).

Jungle words

Look for each of the words below in the letter grid.
Draw a ring around each one when you find it.

panda   snake   lion   tiger

p	q	t	w	s
a	l	i	o	n
n	i	g	o	a
d	a	e	s	k
a	h	r	j	e

Butterfly letters

Look at the letters carefully.
Draw a ring around the odd one out on each butterfly.

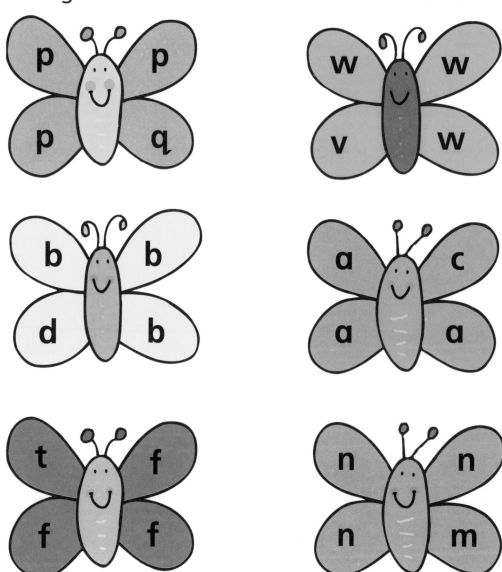

Note for parent: This activity helps children to observe differences in letters.

What do I eat?

Draw the things that you can eat on the table.

 pizza   **snake**   **cake**   **banana**

 sandwich   **ice cream**   **dog**   **football**

How many things did you draw?_____

Which is your favourite food?_____

 Note for parent: This activity helps children to learn food words.

Find the rhymes

Look at the little pictures. Read the words.

plate

ball

frog

Note for parent: This activity helps children understand rhyming pairs.

Draw a line from each picture to something in
the big picture that rhymes.

bee

star

boat

mouse

Yes or no?

Do these pictures rhyme?
Put a ✓ by the ones that rhyme and a ✗ by the ones that do not rhyme. The first one has been done for you.

Note for parent: Rhyming helps children to listen carefully in order to make judgements.

Clothes words

Draw lines to join each picture to the right word.

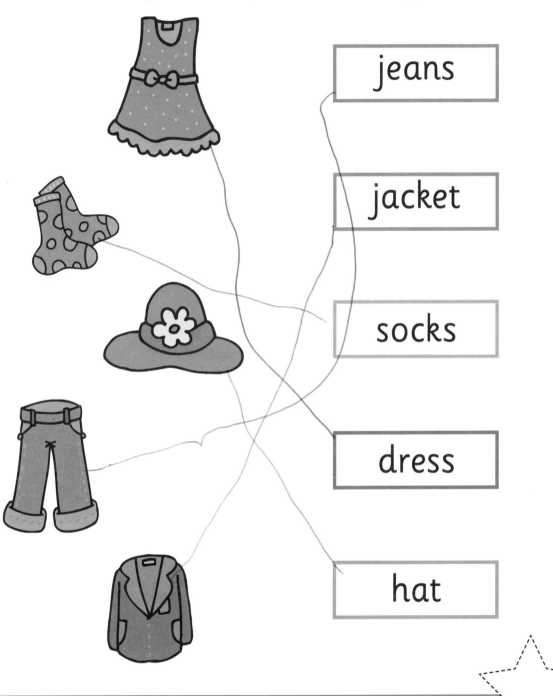

jeans

jacket

socks

dress

hat

 Note for parent: This activity helps children to match words and pictures.

223

Do you remember?

These are all words you have already seen.
Trace each word. Join each picture to the right word.

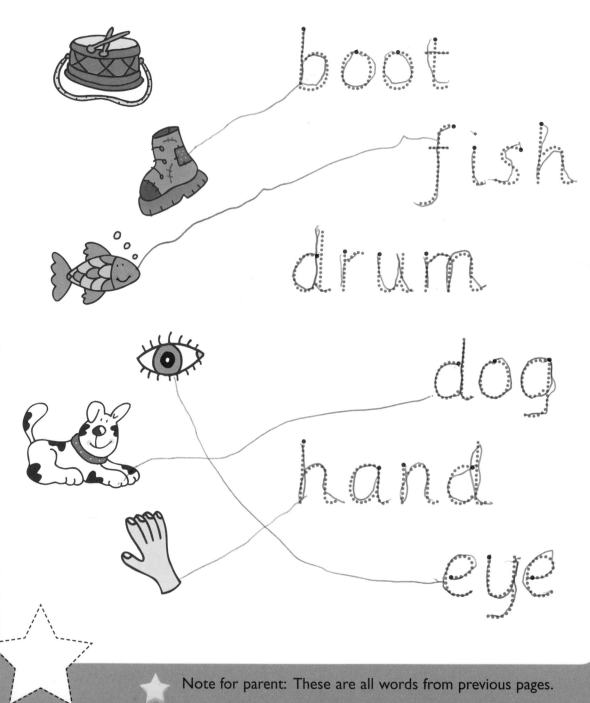

boot

fish

drum

dog

hand

eye

Note for parent: These are all words from previous pages.

True or false?

Look at each picture. Read the sentence. Put a ✓ in the box if it is true and a ✗ if it is false.

Max is at the seaside.

Emma is at the farm.

Clare is at the park.

Peter is at the shops.

 Note for parent: This activity helps children to understand what they are seeing.

Hospital words

Read the words.

✓ the ones you can see in the picture.

✗ the ones you cannot see.

bed ✓

cat ✗

car ✗

Note for parent: This activity encourages discussion and observation.

Colour the picture.

bandage 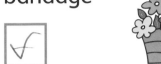 flowers

 nurse bird dog

227

Simple sentences

Use a rhyming word from the box to finish each sentence.

> jar   cat   sun   vet   dish

I am a fat ___cat___

I took my pet to the ___vet___

It is fun to sit in the ___sun___

The star is in a ___jar___

The fish is in a ___dish___

 Note for parent: This page helps children to read simple sentences with picture clues.

Pick the right word

Cross out the word that does not match the picture.

bell

shell

key

bee

make

cake

tree

sea

book

hook

truck

duck

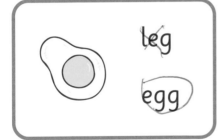

leg

egg

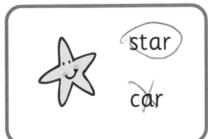

star

car

Note for parent: Recognizing rhymes helps children listen carefully.

More creepy crawlies

These are words you have read before.
See if you can remember them and join them to
the right pictures.

spider   **ant**   **worm**   **bee**

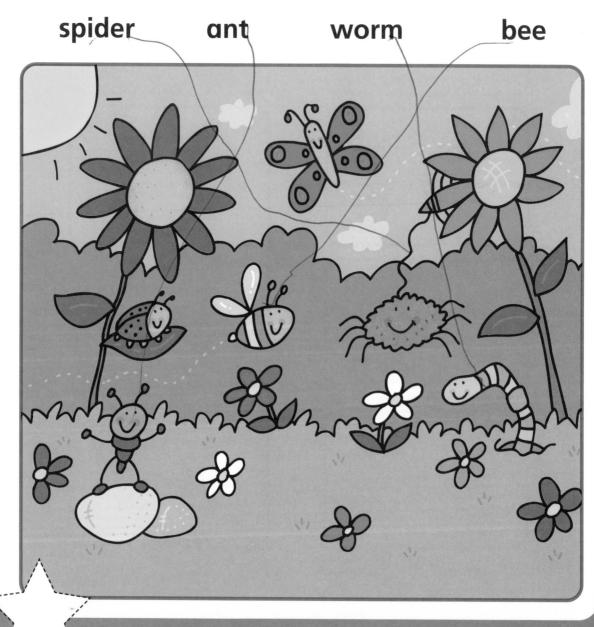

Note for parent: This activity helps children to revise creepy
crawly words. They can refer back to page 211.

Jungle words

These are words you have read before.
See if you can remember them and join them to the
right picture.

panda   **snake**   **lion**   **tiger**

Answers

Page 11
1 ball,
1 dog,
1 bone.

Page 12
2 gloves,
2 shoes,
2 socks.

Page 13

Emma lives at number 2.

Page 14
3 bears,
3 chairs,
3 beds.

Page 15

Page 16

Page 17
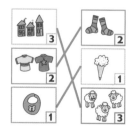

Page 18
4 candles,
4 hooves.

Page 19

✓ ☐ ☐ ☐

Page 20
There are 5 toes.

Page 21

Pages 22–23

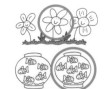

Page 24
The bee has 6 legs.
The hen has 6 eggs.

Page 25

Page 26
There are 7 presents.

Page 27
There are 7 dwarfs.
There are 7 beds.

Page 28
There are 8 socks.
The spider has 8 legs.

Page 29
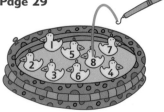

Page 30
There are 9 marbles.

Page 31
7 bees,
9 flags,
8 crayons,
9 ice creams.

Page 32
There are 10 toes.

Page 33
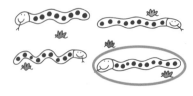

There are 10 bottles.

Pages 34–35
5 frogs,
2 socks,
3 pigs,
1 house,
4 wheels,
9 carrots,
6 eggs,
10 cakes,
7 bats,
8 teddy bears.

Page 41

Pages 42–43

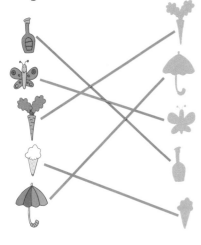

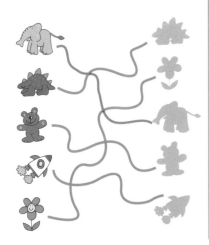

Page 49

Page 51

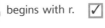

Page 54
Duck begins with the letter d.

Page 55
horse, bee, pig.

Page 56

begins with r. ✓

begins with n. ✗

begins with m. ✗

Page 58
Kite begins with the letter k.

Page 59

Page 61

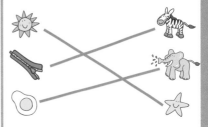

Page 65

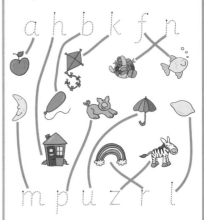

233

Answers

Pages 66–67

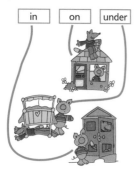

Page 68

| in | on | under |

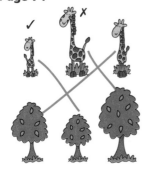

Page 70

The red snake is short.
The green snake is long.

Page 71

Page 72

The elephant and the tractor are heavy.

Page 73

Pages 74-75

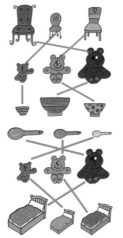

Page 76

There are 2 houses.
There are 3 flags.

Page 77

The number 2 is missing.

Page 79

1 horse, 2 dogs, 3 cats,
4 rabbits, 5 ducks.

Page 80

The blue circle is small.
The purple circle is big.

Page 84

Page 86

yellow square,
blue circle,
green triangle.

Page 87

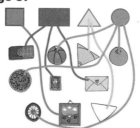

Page 88

Page 89

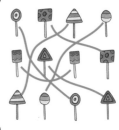

Page 90

There are 5 candles on the cake.

Page 91

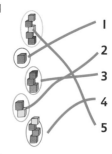

Page 92

Page 93

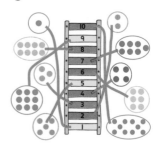

Pages 94–95

Pages 96–97

Page 100

Possible answers are: d – dog, b – ball, h – horse, k – kite, c – cake, a – apple, s – sandwich, f – fox.

Page 101

<u>m</u>an <u>r</u>ing <u>p</u>ig <u>e</u>gg <u>g</u>ate <u>l</u>og

Page 104

Possible answers are: n – nest, z – zebra, t – tiger, f – fox, w – window, o – owl, v – vase, k – kangaroo.

Page 105

a = apple, astronaut; b = boat, ball; c = car, cat; d = duck, dog.
A F H W P B E

Page 106

tree: <u>tr</u>iangle, <u>tr</u>ain, <u>tr</u>actor.
bridge: <u>br</u>ush, <u>br</u>ead, <u>br</u>icks.
flag: <u>fl</u>ipper, <u>fl</u>y, <u>fl</u>ower.

Page 107

<u>f</u>ish, bir<u>d</u>, <u>h</u>at, <u>k</u>ing, <u>t</u>ent, <u>z</u>ebra.

Page 108

hook/book, dog/frog, man/fan, moon/spoon, bee/tree.

Page 109

spider: <u>sp</u>aghetti, <u>sp</u>oon, <u>sp</u>ade.
whale: <u>wh</u>eelbarrow, <u>wh</u>istle, <u>wh</u>eel.
sheep: <u>sh</u>oe, <u>sh</u>ark, <u>sh</u>ell.

Page 110

<u>d</u>ice, <u>b</u>aby, <u>d</u>og, <u>d</u>oor, <u>b</u>all, <u>b</u>ook, <u>d</u>uck, <u>b</u>ed.

Page 111

<u>cl</u>ock/<u>cl</u>oud/<u>cl</u>own;
<u>dr</u>ess/<u>dr</u>agon/<u>dr</u>um;
<u>gr</u>een/<u>gr</u>ass/<u>gr</u>apes.

Page 112

Page 113

hats, socks, bats, balls, trees, stars.

Page 114

be<u>d</u>, do<u>g</u>, su<u>n</u>, boo<u>k</u>, ten<u>t</u>, bu<u>s</u>.

Page 115

Page 116

amb**o**jsr**wcl** – owl, bc**m**sr**ott**on – moon, az**c**ms**o**gk**w**y – cow, en**d**yrmrn**um** – drum.

Page 117

hook/book, dog/frog, man/fan.
book, ball.
bed, dog.

Pages 118–119

Page 120

Page 121

235

Answers

Page 123

Page 124
These people have more:

Page 127
1 + 1 = 2
1 + 1 = 2

Page 131

more holes ✓

more dogs ✓

Pages 132–133
2 flags,
3 apples,
4 butterflies,
5 hats.

Page 136
3 shells,
4 balls,
4 presents.

Page 138
4 boats,
4 trees.

Page 140
5 stars,
5 cars.

Page 142

Page 143

Pages 144–145

4

3

2

I

Page 146
1 crayon is left.

2 balloons are left.

Page 147

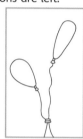

2   I

Pages 148–149

4

3

2

I

Pages 150–151

<u>a</u>stronaut, <u>b</u>anana, <u>c</u>alculator, <u>d</u>inosaur, <u>e</u>lephant, <u>f</u>ish. <u>g</u>ate, <u>h</u>elicopter, <u>i</u>nsect, <u>j</u>uggler, <u>k</u>angaroo, <u>l</u>emon, <u>m</u>agician.

Pages 152–153

<u>n</u>et, <u>o</u>ctopus, <u>p</u>arachute, <u>q</u>ueen, <u>r</u>ainbow, <u>s</u>andwich. <u>t</u>eddy, <u>u</u>mbrella, <u>v</u>ase, <u>w</u>eb, <u>x</u>-ray, <u>y</u>o-yo, <u>z</u>ebra.

Page 154

parrot/pineapple, telephone/toothbrush, kite/king, butterfly/baby, window/watch.

Page 155

The odd ones out are: ball, cat, hat, cake, penguin.

Page 156

f i s h

Page 157

The odd ones out are: box, flag, pear, star, 4.

Page 158

sheep/shoes, chick/chair.

Page 159

<u>a</u>mbulance, <u>v</u>iolin, <u>s</u>ock, <u>n</u>est, <u>j</u>ellyfish, <u>t</u>able, <u>l</u>eaf, <u>c</u>arrot, <u>r</u>ocket, <u>d</u>uck.

Page 160

<u>c</u>at, <u>m</u>at, <u>h</u>at, <u>b</u>at, <u>r</u>at, <u>b</u>at.

Page 161

begins with f ✔
begins with m ✘
begins with b ✔
begins with d ✔
begins with w ✘
begins with l ✔

Page 162

co<u>w</u>, train, mo<u>p</u>, pig, cra<u>b</u>, ten<u>t</u>, su<u>n</u>, bir<u>d</u>.

Page 163

parrot/pineapple, kite/king, window/watch. <u>a</u>mbulance, <u>t</u>able, <u>v</u>iolin, <u>l</u>eaf.

Page 164

snail–nail, donkey–key, rainbow–rain or bow, starfish–star or fish.

Page 165

dog, mop, hat, bus, egg, cup, pig, sun.

Page 166

church/cheese, sheep/shell, chick/chair, shoes/shark, cherries/chocolate.

Page 167

chair, sheep, shoes, church, chick.

Page 168

throne, thirteen, three, thermometer.

Page 169

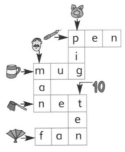

Page 170

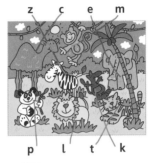

Page 171

cup–p, net–t, dog–g, map–p, bus–s, fan–n.

Pages 172

c	o	w	d	i	m
j	r	b	a	t	l
w	s	u	n	f	j
z	i	s	p	k	u
y	x	v	e	g	g
h	q	t	g	n	p

Page 173

shoe<u>s</u>, hat<u>s</u>, glove<u>s</u>, coat<u>s</u>.

Page 174

<u>ch</u>air, <u>sh</u>eep, <u>sh</u>oes. dog, mop, hat, bus. cup–p, net–t, dog–g, map–p.

Page 175

<u>sh</u>oes, wat<u>ch</u>, bru<u>sh</u>, <u>th</u>umb, <u>ch</u>air, too<u>th</u>. The odd one out is: church.

Page 176

These words should be crossed out: ball, hut, fos, pin, kat, men. pig, web.

Page 177

Possible answers are: <u>b</u>ed, <u>c</u>omputer, <u>d</u>inosaur, <u>n</u>et. card, plug, book, basket. chair, shell, three.

237

Answers

Page 186

Page 187
Colours used:
yellow,
blue,
purple,
red,
green.

Page 188

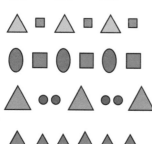

square

circle

diamond

rectangle

Page 189
These shapes are needed to finish the patterns:

Page 190
6,
circles.

Page 195

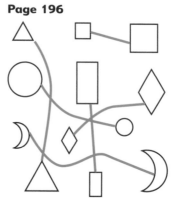

Page 196

Page 198

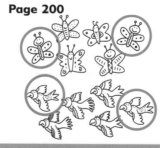

Page 200

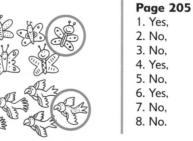

Page 201

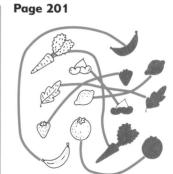

Page 203

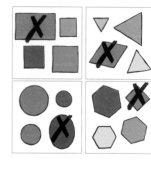

Page 204

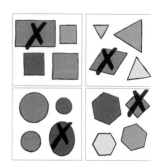

Page 205
1. Yes,
2. No,
3. No,
4. Yes,
5. No,
6. Yes,
7. No,
8. No.

Page 206

wall–ball, mouse–house, coat–boat, bat–cat, chicks–bricks, star–car.

Page 207

eye = 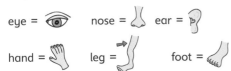 nose = ear =

hand = leg = foot =

Page 208

These words should be circled: train, clock, frog, car, duck.

Page 209

bat–cat, hen–ten, ball–wall, leg–egg.

Page 211

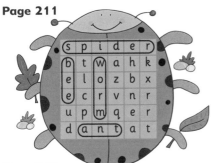

Page 212

Page 213

These things are big:

Page 214

Muffet–tuffet, diddle–fiddle, Horner–corner, roses–posies.

Page 217

Page 218

These letters are the odd ones out: q, v, d, c, t, m.

Page 219

There are five things you can eat: pizza, cake, banana, sandwich, ice cream.

Page 220

plate   ball   frog   bee   mouse   boat   star

Page 222

These are the words that rhyme: moon–spoon, star–car, nail–snail.

Page 223

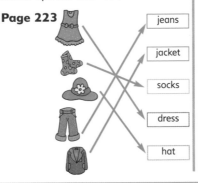

jeans

jacket

socks

dress

hat

Page 224

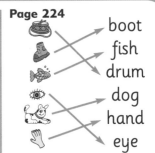

boot
fish
drum
dog
hand
eye

Page 225

Max is at the seaside = ✓
Emma is at the farm = ✗
Clare is at the park = ✗
Peter is at the shops = ✓

Page 226

bed =✓, cat =✗, car =✗, bandage =✓, nurse =✓, flowers =✓, bird =✗, dog =✗.

Page 228

I am a fat cat.
I took my pet to the vet.
It is fun to sit in the sun.
The star is in a jar.
The fish is in a dish.

Page 229

These words should be crossed out: shell, bee, make, sea, hook, truck, leg, car.

Page 230

spider   ant   worm   bee

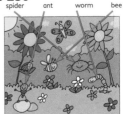

Page 231

panda   snake   lion   tiger

The End